Best in Children's Books

Garden City, New York 9

June 2d 1904.

The Boy King Arthur

by MARY MACLEOD

illustrated by HENRY C. PITZ

THE MARVEL OF THE SWORD

When Uther Pendragon, King of England, died, the country for a long while stood in great danger, for every lord that was mighty gathered his forces, and many wished to be King. For King Uther's own son, Prince Arthur, who

A selection from *The Book of King Arthur and His Noble Knights: Stories from Sir Thomas Mallory's Morte d'Arthur,* published by Wells Gardner, Darton & Co., Ltd., London, England.

should have succeeded him, was but a child, and Merlin, the mighty magician, had hidden him away.

Now a strange thing had happened at Arthur's birth, and this was how it was.

Some time before, Merlin had done Uther a great service, on condition that the King should grant him whatever he wished for. This the King swore a solemn oath to do. Then Merlin made him promise that when his child was born, it should be delivered to Merlin to bring up as he chose for this would be to the child's own advantage. The King

had given his promise so he was obliged to agree. Then Merlin said he knew a very true and faithful man, one of King Uther's lords, by name Sir Ector, who had large possessions in many parts of England and Wales, and that the child should be given to him to bring up.

On the night the baby was born, while it was still unchristened, King Uther commanded two knights and two ladies to take it, wrapped in a cloth of gold, and deliver it to a poor man whom they would find waiting at the gate of the Castle. This poor man was Merlin in disguise, although they did not know it. So the child was delivered unto Merlin and he carried him to Sir Ector, and made a holy man christen him, and named him Arthur; and Sir Ector's wife cherished him as her own child.

Within two years King Uther fell sick of a great malady, and for three days and three nights he was speechless. All the Barons were in much sorrow, and asked Merlin what was best to be done.

"There is no remedy," said Merlin, "God will have His Will. But look ye all, Barons, come before King Uther to-morrow, and God will make him speak."

So the next day Merlin and all the Barons came before the King, and Merlin said aloud to King Uther: "Sir, after your days shall your son Arthur be King of this realm and all that belongs to it?"

Then Uther Pendragon turned to him and said in hearing of them all: "I give my son, Arthur, God's blessing and mine, and bid him pray for my soul, and righteously and honourably claim the Crown, or forfeit my blessing."

And with that, King Uther died.

But Arthur was still only a baby, not two years old, and Merlin knew it would be no use yet to proclaim him King. For there were many powerful nobles in England in those days who were all trying to get the kingdom for themselves, and perhaps they would kill the little Prince. So there was much strife and debate in the land.

When several years had passed, Merlin went to the Archbishop of Canterbury and counselled him to send for all the lords of the realm, and all the gentlemen of arms, that they should come to London at Christmas, and for this cause—that a miracle would show who should be rightly King of the realm. So all the lords and gentlemen made themselves ready, and came to London, and long before dawn on Christmas Day they were all gathered in the great church of St. Paul to pray.

When the first service was over, there was seen in the churchyard a large stone, four-square, like marble, and in the midst of it was an anvil of steel, a foot high. In this was stuck by the point a beautiful sword, with naked blade, and there were letters written in gold about the sword, which said thus:

> "*Whoso pulleth this sword*
> *out of this stone and anvil*
> *is rightly King of all England.*"

Then the people marvelled, and told the Archbishop.

"I command," said the Archbishop, "that you keep within the church, and pray unto God still; and that no man touch the sword till the service is over."

So when the prayers in church were over, all the lords went to behold the stone and the sword; and when they read the writing, some of them—such as wished to be King—tried to pull the sword out of the anvil. But not one could make it stir.

"The man is not here that shall achieve the sword," said the Archbishop, "but, doubt not, God will make him known. But let us provide ten knights, men of good fame, to keep guard over the sword."

So it was ordained, and proclamation was made that everyone who wished might try to win the sword. And upon New Year's Day the Barons arranged to have a great tournament, in which all knights who would joust might take a part. This was ordained to keep together the Lords and Commons, for the Archbishop trusted that it would be made known who should win the sword.

On New Year's Day, after church, the Barons rode to the field, some to joust, and some to tourney, and so it happened that Sir Ector, who had large estates near London, came also to the tournament; and with him rode Sir Kay, his son, with young Arthur, his foster brother.

As they rode, Sir Kay found he had lost his sword, for he had left it at his father's lodging, so he begged young Arthur to go and fetch it for him.

"That will I, gladly," said Arthur, and he rode fast away.

But when he came to the house, he found no one at home to give him the sword, for everyone had gone to see the jousting. Then Arthur was angry and said to himself: "I will ride to the churchyard, and take the sword with me that sticketh in the stone, for my brother, Sir Kay, shall not be without a sword this day."

When he came to the churchyard he alighted, and tied his horse to the stile, and went to the tent. But he found there no knights guarding the sword, for they were all away at the joust. Seizing the sword by the handle, he lightly and fiercely pulled it out of the stone. Then he took his horse and rode his way, till he came to Sir Kay, his brother, to whom he delivered the sword.

As soon as Sir Kay saw it, he knew well it was the sword of the stone. He rode to his father, Sir Ector, and said: "Sir, lo, here is the sword of the stone, wherefore I must be King of this land."

When Sir Ector saw the sword he turned back, and came to the church. There they all three alighted and went into the church, and Sir Ector made his son swear truly how he got the sword.

"By my brother Arthur," said Sir Kay, "for he brought it to me."

"How did you get this sword?" said Sir Ector to Arthur. And the boy told him.

"Now," said Sir Ector, "I understand. You must be King of this land."

"Wherefore I," said Arthur, "and for what cause?"

"Sir," said Ector, "because God will have it so; for no man could draw out this sword except he that shall rightly be King. Now let me see whether you can put the sword there as it was, and pull it out again."

"There is no difficulty," said Arthur, and he put it back into the stone.

Then Sir Ector tried to pull out the sword, and failed. Sir Kay also pulled with all his might, but it would not move.

"Now you shall try," said Sir Ector to Arthur.

"I will, well," said Arthur, and withdrew the sword easily.

At this Sir Ector and Sir Kay knelt down on the ground before him.

"Alas," said Arthur, "mine own dear father and brother, why do you kneel to me?"

"Nay, nay, my lord Arthur, it is not so. I was never your father, nor of your blood; but I know well you are of higher blood than I thought you were."

Then Sir Ector told him all, how he had taken him to bring up, and by whose command; and how he had received him from Merlin. And when he understood that Ector was not his father, Arthur was deeply grieved.

"Will you be my good, gracious lord, when you are King?" asked the knight.

"If not, I should be to blame," said Arthur, "for you are the man in the world to whom I am the most beholden, and my good lady and mother, your wife, who has fostered and kept me as well as her own children. And if ever it be God's will that I be King, as you say, you shall desire of me whatever you wish, and I shall not fail you. God forbid I should fail you."

"Sir," said Sir Ector, "I will ask no more of you but that you will make my son, your foster brother, Sir Kay, seneschal of all your lands."

"That shall be done," said Arthur, "and by my faith no man but he shall have that office while he and I live."

Then they went to the Archbishop and told him how the sword was achieved, and by whom.

On Twelfth Day, all the Barons came to the stone in the churchyard, so that any who wished might try to win the sword. But not one of them could take it out, except Arthur. Many of them, therefore, were very angry, and said it was a great shame to them and to the country to be governed by a boy not of high blood, for as yet none of them knew that he was the son of King Uther Pendragon. So they agreed to delay the decision till Candlemas, which is the second day of February.

But when Candlemas came, and Arthur once more was the only one who could pull out the sword, they put it off till Easter; and when Easter came and Arthur again prevailed, they put it off till the Feast of Pentecost.

Then by Merlin's advice, the Archbishop summoned

some of the best knights that were to be got—such knights as in his own day King Uther Pendragon had best loved, and trusted most—and these were appointed to attend young Arthur, and never to leave him night or day till the Feast of Pentecost.

When the great day came, all manner of men once more made the attempt, and once more not one of them could prevail except Arthur. Before all the Lords and Commons there assembled, he pulled out the sword, whereupon all the Commons cried out at once: "We will have Arthur for our King! We will put him no more in delay, for we see that it is God's will that he shall be our King, and he who holdeth against it, we will slay him."

And therewith they knelt down, both rich and poor, and besought pardon of Arthur, because they had delayed him so long.

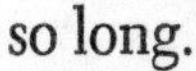

And Arthur forgave them, and took the sword in both his hands, and offered it on the altar where the Archbishop was, and so he was made knight by the best man there.

After that, he was crowned at once, and there he swore to his Lords and Commons to be a true King, and to govern with true justice from thenceforth all the days of his life.

THE SIEGE OF THE STRONG TOWER

After Arthur was crowned King, many complaints were made to him of great wrongs that had been done since the death of King Uther; many Lords, Knights, Ladies and Gentlemen having been deprived of their lands. Thereupon King Arthur caused the lands to be given again to them that owned them. When this was done, and all the districts round London were settled, he made Sir Kay, Seneschal of England; Sir Baldwin, Constable of Britain; and Sir Ulfius, Chamberlain; while Sir Brastias was appointed Warden of the country north of the Trent. Most of this land was then held by the King's enemies, but within a few years Arthur had won all the north.

Then King Arthur went into Wales, and proclaimed a great feast, to be held at Pentecost, after his crowning in the city of Carleon. To this feast came many rich and powerful Kings, with great retinues of knights. Arthur was glad of their coming, for he thought that the Kings and the knights had come in love, and to do him honour at his feast, wherefore he rejoiced, and sent them rich presents.

The Kings, however, would receive none of them, but rebuked the messengers shamefully, saying it gave them no pleasure to receive gifts from a beardless boy of low blood. They sent him word that they would have none of his gifts, but they would come and give him gifts with hard swords betwixt the neck and the shoulders. It was for that they came hither, so they told the messengers plainly, for it was a great shame to them all to see such a boy have the rule of so noble a realm as this land.

When the messengers brought this answer to King Arthur, by the advice of his Barons he betook himself with five hundred good men to a strong tower. And all the Kings laid siege to him, but King Arthur had plenty of food.

Within fifteen days Merlin, the great magician, came into the city of Carleon. All the Kings were very glad to see him, and asked him: "For what cause is that boy Arthur made your King?"

"Sirs," said Merlin, "I will tell you the cause, because he is King Uther Pendragon's son. And whosoever saith 'Nay,' Arthur shall be King, and overcome all his enemies, and before he dies he shall long have been King of all England, and have under his sway Wales, Ireland, and Scotland, and more realms than I will now relate."

Some of the Kings marvelled at Merlin's words, and deemed it well that it should be as he said; and some of them, such as King Lot of Orkney, laughed at him and called him a wizard. But they all consented that King Arthur should come out and speak with them, and gave their assurance that he should come and return safely.

So Merlin went to King Arthur, and told him what he had done, and bade him come out boldly and speak with them.

"Spare them not," he said, "but answer them as their King and Chieftain, for ye shall overcome them all, whether they will or not."

Then King Arthur came out of his tower, having under his gown a cuirass of double mail; and there went with him the Archbishop of Canterbury, and Sir Baldwin, Sir Kay, and Sir Brastias. When he met the Kings, there were stout words on both sides; King Arthur ready with an answer to all they said, and declaring that if he lived, he would make them bow. They departed therefore in wrath, and King Arthur returned to the tower where he armed himself and all his knights.

"What will you do?" said Merlin to the Kings. "You had better refrain, for you will not prevail here, were you ten times as many."

"Are we well advised to be afraid of a dream-reader?" sneered King Lot.

With that, Merlin vanished away, and came to King Arthur, and bade him set on them fiercely. And the magician counselled Arthur not to fight at first with the sword he had got by miracle; but if he found himself getting the worst of the fight, then to draw it and do his best.

Meanwhile, three hundred of the best men who were with the Kings went to join Arthur, and this comforted him greatly. All his knights fought gallantly, and the battle raged with fury. King Arthur, himself, was ever in the foremost of the press, till his horse was slain underneath him.

And therewith King Lot smote down King Arthur.

Four of his knights rescued him and set him on horseback. Then he drew forth his sword, and it was so bright in his enemies' eyes that it gave light like thirty torches; and thus he drove back his foes and slew many of them.

Then the citizens of Carleon arose with clubs and stones, and slew many knights. But all the Kings banded together with their knights who were alive, and so fled and departed.

And Merlin came to Arthur, and counselled him to follow them no further.

After the feast and the tourney, Arthur came to London, and called all his Barons to a Council. For Merlin had told him that the six Kings who had made war upon him, and whom he had defeated, would hasten to wreak their vengeance on him and his lands. The Barons could give no counsel, but said they would fight.

"You say well," said Arthur. "I thank you for your good courage; but will all of you who love me speak with Merlin? You know well that he has done much for me, and knows many things, and when he is with you I wish that you would beseech him to give you his best advice."

All the Barons said they would gladly hear what Merlin counselled, so the magician was sent for.

"I warn you well," said Merlin, "that your enemies are passing strong and are as good men of arms as any alive. By this time, too, they have got to themselves four Kings more and a mighty Duke. Unless our King can get more knights than are now to be found within the bounds of his own realm, if he fight these Kings in battle he shall be overcome and slain."

"What is best to be done?" asked the Barons.

"I will tell you my advice," said Merlin. "There are two brethren beyond the sea, and they are both Kings, and marvellously powerful men. One is called King Ban of Benwick, and the other, King Bors of Gaul—that is, France. And against these two brothers wars a mighty man, the King Claudas, and strives with them for a castle; and there is great war betwixt them. But because Claudas is very rich he gets many good knights to fight for him, and for the most part puts these two Kings to the worse. Now this is my counsel—that our King send to Kings Ban and Bors two trusty knights, with letters stating that if they will come and see Arthur and his Court, and help him in his wars, then he will swear to help them against King Claudas. Now, what do you say to this counsel?"

"This is well counselled," said the King and the Barons.

So in all haste it was settled.

Ulfius and Brastias were chosen as the messengers, and they rode forth well-horsed and well-armed; and so crossed the sea and rode towards the city of Benwick. Here, in a narrow place, they were attacked by eight knights of King Claudas, who tried to kill them or take them prisoners. But Ulfius and Brastias, fighting with them two by two, in turn overcame them all, and left them lying sorely hurt and bruised on the field.

When they came to Benwick, it fortunately happened that both the Kings, Ban and Bors, were there. As soon as the Kings knew they were messengers of Arthur, they gave them the very heartiest greeting, and when Ban and Bors read the letters, they were made even more welcome.

So Ulfius and Brastias had good cheer, and rich gifts, as many as they could carry away, and they took back this answer with them—that the two Kings would come to Arthur in all the haste they could.

King Arthur was very glad to get this message, and when the time came for the Kings to arrive, he proclaimed a great feast and went ten miles out of London to meet them. After the feast there was a splendid tournament, in which seven hundred knights took part. Arthur, Ban, and Bors, with the Archbishop of Canterbury, and Sir Ector sat in a place covered with cloth of gold, like a hall, with ladies and gentlewomen, to behold who did best. The knights who won the prizes were three of King Arthur's household, Sir Kay, Sir Lucas, and Sir Griflet.

With the help of King Ban and King Bors, Arthur utterly defeated and put to rout the eleven Kings who were warring against him. When his enemies were scattered, King Ban and King Bors, laden with rich gifts, returned to their own countries. And they made a compact with Arthur that if they had need of him to help them against King Claudas, they would send to him for succour; and on the other hand, if Arthur had need of them, he was to send, and they would not tarry.

One day there had come to the Court a squire on horseback, leading a knight before him, wounded to death. He told how there was a knight in the forest who had reared a pavilion by a fountain, and how he had slain his master, a good knight; and he besought that his master might be buried, and some knight might revenge his death.

A young squire called Griflet came to the King, and besought him to make him a knight.

"Thou art full young and tender," said Arthur, "to take so high an order on thee."

"Sir," said Griflet, "I beseech you to make me a knight."

"Sir, it were great pity to lose Griflet," said Merlin, "for he will be a passing good man when he is of age, abiding with you the term of his life."

So the King made him a knight.

"Now," he said, "since I have made you a knight, you must give me a gift."

"What you will," said Griflet.

Then the King made him promise that when he had fought with the knight at the fountain he would return straight to the Court without further debate.

So Griflet took his horse in great haste, and got ready his shield, and took a spear in his hand, and rode at a gallop till he came to the fountain. There he saw a rich pavilion, and near by under a cloth stood a fair horse, well-saddled and bridled, and on a tree a shield of many colours, and a great spear. Griflet smote on the shield with the butt of his spear, so that the shield fell to the ground.

With that, the knight came out of the pavilion, and said: "Fair knight, why smote you down my shield?"

"Because I would joust with you," said Griflet.

"It is better you do not," said the knight, "for you are but young and lately made a knight, and your might is nothing to mine."

"As for that," said Griflet, "I *will* joust with you."

"I am loath to do it," said the knight, "but since I needs must, I will make ready. Whence be ye?"

"Sir, I am of Arthur's Court."

The two knights ran together, so that Griflet's spear was all shivered to pieces. Therewith the other knight, whose name was Pellinore, smote Griflet through the shield and left side, and broke his own spear, while horse and knight fell down.

When Pellinore saw Griflet lie so on the ground, he alighted, and he was sad, for he thought he had slain him. He unlaced his helm, and gave him air, and set him again on his horse, saying that Griflet had a mighty heart, and if he lived he would prove a passing good knight. So Sir Griflet rode back to Court. And through good doctors, he was healed and saved.

King Arthur was very wrathful because of the hurt to Sir Griflet, and he commanded one of his men to have his horse and armour ready waiting for him outside the city before daylight on the following morning. On the morrow, before dawn, he mounted and took spear and shield, telling the man to wait there till he came again

He rode softly till day, and then he saw Merlin being chased by three churls, who would have slain him. The King rode towards them, and they were frightened when they saw a knight, and fled.

"O Merlin," said Arthur, "for all thy crafts, thou hadst been slain had I not been here!"

"Nay, not so," said Merlin, "for I could save myself if I would. And thou art nearer thy death than I am, for thou art going towards thy death, if God be not thy friend."

As they went thus talking they came to the fountain and the rich pavilion there beside it. Then King Arthur was aware of an armed knight who sat there.

"Sir Knight," said Arthur, "for what cause abidest thou here so that no knight may ride this way unless he joust with thee? I counsel thee to leave this custom."

"This custom," said Pellinore, "I have used, and will use, despite who saith nay; and whoever liketh not my custom, let him mend it."

"I will amend it," said Arthur.

"I shall prevent you," said Pellinore.

He quickly mounted his horse, adjusted his shield, and took his spear. They met so hard against each other's shields

that their spears shivered. Thereupon Arthur at once pulled out his sword.

"Nay, not so," said the knight, "it is fairer that we twain run once more together with sharp spears."

"I would readily," said Arthur, "had I more spears."

"I have enough," said Pellinore.

A squire came and brought two good spears, and again the knight and the King spurred together with all their might, so that both the spears were broken off short. Then Arthur set hand on his sword.

"Nay," said the knight, "ye shall do better. Ye are a passing good jouster as ever I met withal, and for the love of the high order of knighthood let us joust once again."

"I assent," said Arthur.

Then two more great spears were brought. Each knight took one, and they ran together, so that Arthur's spear was all shivered. But Pellinore hit him so hard in the shield that horse and man fell to the earth. Then Arthur eagerly

pulled out his sword, saying, "I will assay thee, Sir Knight, on foot, for I have lost the honour on horseback." And he ran towards him with his sword drawn.

When Pellinore saw that, he too alighted, for he thought it no honour to have a knight at such disadvantage, for himself to be on horseback, and the other on foot. Then began a strong battle with many great strokes, both hacking and hewing, till the field was wet with blood. They fought long, and rested, and then went to battle again. At last they both smote together, so that their swords met evenly, but Pellinore's sword smote Arthur's in two pieces, wherefore the King was much grieved.

Then said the knight unto Arthur: "Thou art in danger whether I choose to save thee or to slay thee; and unless thou yield thee as overcome and recreant, thou shalt die."

"As for death," said King Arthur, "welcome be it, when it cometh; but to yield me unto thee, I had rather die than be so shamed." And with that he leapt unto Pellinore, and threw him down, and tore off his helm.

When the knight felt this he was sorely frightened, though he was a very big and mighty man; but he quickly got Arthur underneath, and raised his helm, and would have smitten off his head.

But up came Merlin, and said: "Knight, hold thy hand, for if thou slay that knight, thou puttest this realm in the greatest damage that ever realm was in. For this knight is a man of more renown than thou art aware of."

"Why, who is he?" said Pellinore.

"It is King Arthur."

Then Pellinore would have slain himself, and lifted up his sword. But Merlin cast an enchantment on the knight, so that he fell to the earth in a great sleep.

THE SWORD EXCALIBUR

After throwing Pellinore into an enchanted sleep, Merlin took up King Arthur and rode forth on Pellinore's horse.

"Alas!" said Arthur. "What hast thou done, Merlin? Hast thou slain this good knight by thy crafts? There lived not so worshipful a knight as he was. I would rather than a year's income that he were alive."

"Do not be troubled," said Merlin, "for he is less hurt than you. He is only asleep, and will awake within three hours. There liveth not a greater knight than he is, and he shall hereafter do you right good service. His name is Pellinore, and he shall have two sons, that shall be good men—

Percival of Wales, and Lamerack of Wales."

Leaving Sir Pellinore, King Arthur and Merlin went to a hermit, who was a good man, and skilled in the art of healing. He attended so carefully to the King's wounds, that in three days they were quite well, and Arthur was able to go on his way with Merlin. Then as they rode, Arthur said, "I have no sword."

"No matter," said Merlin, "nearby is a sword that shall be yours if I can get it."

So they rode till they came to a lake, which was a fair water and broad; and in the midst of the lake, Arthur saw an arm, clothed in white samite, that held in its hand a beautiful sword.

"Lo," said Merlin, "yonder is the sword I spoke of."

With that they saw a damsel rowing across the lake.

"What damsel is that?" said Arthur.

"That is the Lady of the Lake," said Merlin, "and within that lake is a rock, and therein is as fair a place as any on earth, and richly adorned. This damsel will soon come to you; then speak you fair to her, so that she will give you that sword."

Presently the damsel came to Arthur, and saluted him, and he her again.

"Damsel," said Arthur, "what sword is that which yonder the arm holdeth above the water? I would it were mine, for I have no sword."

"Sir Arthur, King," said the damsel, "that sword is mine; the name of it is Excalibur, that is as much as to say *Cut-Steel*. If you will give me a gift when I ask you, ye shall have it."

"By my faith," said Arthur, "I will give you what gift ye shall ask."

"Well," said the damsel, "go you into yonder barge, and row yourself to the sword, and take it and the scabbard with you, and I will ask my gift when I see my time."

So King Arthur and Merlin alighted, and tied their horses to two trees, and went into the barge, and when they came to the sword that the hand held, Arthur lifted it and took it with him. And the arm and hand went under the water; and so they came to the land, and rode away.

Then King Arthur looked on the sword, and liked it passing well.

"Which like you the better, the sword or the scabbard?" asked Merlin.

"I like the sword better," replied Arthur.

"You are the more unwise," said Merlin, "for the scabbard is worth ten of the sword. While you have the scabbard upon you, ye shall never lose any blood, be ye ever so sorely wounded. Therefore keep well the scabbard always with you."

So they returned to Carleon, where King Arthur's knights were passing glad to see him. When they heard of his adventures, they marvelled that he would so jeopardize himself alone. But all men of honour said it was merry to be under such a chieftain who would put his person in adventures as other poor knights did.

THE ROUND TABLE

When Arthur had been King for some years, and had fought and overcome many of his enemies, his Barons were anxious that he should take a wife, so according to his usual custom he went and consulted Merlin.

"It is well," said Merlin, "for a man of your bounty and nobleness should not be without a wife. Now is there any that you love more than another?"

"Yes," said King Arthur, "I love Guinevere, the daughter of King Leodegrance, of the land of Cameliard. Leodegrance holdeth in his house the Table Round, which he had of my father, Uther, and this damsel is the most noble and beautiful that I know living."

"Sir," said Merlin, "as to her beauty, she is one of the fairest alive. But if you loved her not as well as you do, I could find you a damsel of beauty and goodness, that would like you and please you—if your heart were not set. But where a man's heart is set, he will be loath to go back."

"That is truth," said King Arthur.

So Merlin carried a message to Leodegrance, who said: "Those are the best tidings I ever heard, that a King of prowess and nobleness will wed my daughter. And as for my lands, I would give him them if I thought it would please him, but he needeth none. I shall send him a gift which shall please him much more. For I shall give him the Round Table which Uther Pendragon gave me, and when it is full, there are a hundred knights and fifty. As for a hundred good knights, I have them, but I lack fifty, for so many have been slain in my days."

So King Leodegrance delivered his daughter to Merlin, and the Round Table, with the hundred knights. And they rode briskly, with great royalty, by water and by land, till they came near to London.

When King Arthur heard of the coming of Guinevere, and the hundred knights with the Round Table, he made great joy because of their coming, and that rich present.

"This fair lady is passing welcome unto me," he said, "for I have loved her long, and therefore there is nothing so dear to me. And these knights with the Round Table please me more than right great riches."

Then in all haste the King commanded preparations for the marriage and coronation to be made in the most honourable way that could be devised; and he bade Merlin go forth and seek fifty knights of the greatest prowess and honour to fill the vacant places at the Round Table.

Within a short time Merlin had found such knights as would fill twenty-eight places, but no more could he find.

Then the Archbishop of Canterbury was fetched, and he blessed the seats with great splendour and devotion, and there sat the eight-and-twenty knights in their seats.

When this was done, Merlin said: "Fair sirs, ye must all arise and come to King Arthur to do him homage," so they arose and did their homage.

And when they were gone Merlin found in every seat letters of gold, that told the knights' names that had sat there; but two places were empty.

Then King Arthur asked Merlin what was the cause why there were two places empty among the seats at the Round Table.

"Sir," said Merlin, "no man shall sit in those places, except he be of the greatest honour."

Therewith Merlin took Sir Pellinore by the hand, and leading him next the two seats he said in open audience: "This is your place, and best worthy ye are to sit therein of any that is here."

Then was the high feast made ready, and the King was wedded at Camelot to Dame Guinevere, in the church of St. Stephen's, with great solemnity.

Then the King established all his knights, and to those who were not rich he gave lands. He charged them never to do outrage nor murders and always to flee treason. Also by no means to be cruel, but to give mercy to him that asked mercy lest they forfeit their honour and the lordship of King Arthur forevermore; and always to succour the ladies, damsels, and gentlewomen, upon pain of death. Also that no man should take battle in a wrongful quarrel for any law, nor for world's goods.

Unto this were all the Knights of the Round Table sworn, both old and young. And every year they renewed their vows at the high Feast of Pentecost.

Baby Bear

by HAMILTON WILLIAMSON

illustrated by FEODOR ROJANKOVSKY

I am Bimba, a baby bear.
I live in a deep jungle.
It's a beautiful place, but I have to watch out and remember that

BEES are there too,

and hungry lions, and

hungry tigers.

Well, one day I forgot, and I said to myself, "I'll–get me a taste of honey."

So I climbed up a tree and was just going to stick my paw into some lovely honeycomb when——bees came flying from everywhere.

They were very angry.

They stung me on the nose, and it got so big I could see it with both my eyes.

My! but it hurt! I felt so bad I thought I had better get me a coconut right away.

So I climbed up a tree that was near a little jungle house and I was just going to put my paw on a nice ripe coconut when a boy ran out.

He had a long spear and a monkey he'd trained to pick the coconuts. I was scared! The monkey started climbing up on one side, and I started climbing down on the other side, when what do you think I saw

? ? ? ? ?

A hungry TIGER waiting for ME!

His skin was all loose, and he wanted to eat me so I would tighten his stripes.

I hurried up the tree again, and guess what happened next.

The monkey saw me!

He screeched to tell the boy on me.

The boy looked, and what should he see but the tiger!

He threw his spear at it and yelled.

His papa came out, and his mamma came out, and they made a big noise.

The tiger ran for his life.

Then I got down, and pretty soon where do you think I was?

HOME.

My! but my mother was glad!

She spanked me and mended my hurting nose.

And for my supper, she gave me honey.

YUM!

Joyful Poems

illustrated by

ALDREN A. WATSON

GIRLS AND BOYS COME OUT TO PLAY

Girls and boys come out to play,
The moon doth shine as bright as day.
Leave your supper and leave your sleep,
And come with your playfellows into the street.
Come with a whoop, come with a call,
Come with a good will or not at all.
Up the ladder and down the wall,
A halfpenny roll will serve us all;
You find milk, and I'll find flour,
And we'll have a pudding in half an hour.

MOTHER GOOSE RHYME

LAUGHING SONG

When the green woods laugh with the voice of joy
And the dimpling stream runs laughing by,
When the air does laugh with our merry wit,
And the green hill laughs with the noise of it,

When the meadows laugh with lively green
And the grasshopper laughs in the merry scene,
When Mary and Susan and Emily,
With their sweet round mouths sing Ha, Ha, He,

When the painted birds laugh in the shade
Where our table with cherries and nuts is spread
Come live and be merry and join with me,
To sing the sweet chorus of Ha, Ha, He.

WILLIAM BLAKE

THE WONDERFUL WORLD

Great, wide, beautiful, wonderful World,
With the wonderful water round you curled,
And the wonderful grass upon your breast,
World, you are beautifully dressed.

The wonderful air is over me,
And the wonderful wind is shaking the tree–
It walks on the water, and whirls the mills,
And talks to itself on the top of the hills.

You friendly Earth, how far do you go,
With the wheat fields that nod and the rivers that flow,
With cities and gardens and cliffs and isles,
And the people upon you for thousands of miles?

Ah! you are so great, and I am so small,
I hardly can think of you, World, at all;
And yet, when I said my prayers today,
My mother kissed me, and said, quite gay,

"If the wonderful World is great to you,
And great to Father and Mother, too,
You are more than the Earth, though you are such a dot!
You can love and think, and the Earth cannot!"

WILLIAM BRIGHTY RANDS

WISHING

Ring–ting! I wish I were a primrose,
A bright yellow primrose blooming in the spring!
The stooping boughs above me,
The wandering bee to love me,
The fern and moss to creep across,
And the elm tree for our king!

Nay–stay! I wish I were an elm tree,
A great, loftly elm tree with green leaves gay!
The winds would set them dancing,
The sun and moonshine glance in,
The birds would house among the boughs,
And ever sweetly sing!

Oh—no! I wish I were a robin,
A robin or a little wren, everywhere to go;
Through forest, field, or garden,
And ask no leave or pardon,
Till winter comes with icy thumbs
To ruffle up our wings!

Well—tell! Where should I fly to,
Where go to sleep in the dark wood or dell?
Before a day was over,
Home comes the rover,
For Mother's kiss—sweeter this
Than any other thing.

WILLIAM ALLINGHAM

"WHERE THE BEE SUCKS"

Where the bee sucks, there suck I;
In a cowslip's bell I lie;
There I couch when owls do cry,
On the bat's back I do fly
After summer merrily;
Merrily, merrily shall I live now,
Under the blossom that hangs on the bough.

WILLIAM SHAKESPEARE

THE BUTTERFLY'S BALL

"Come, take up your hats, and away let us haste
To the Butterfly's Ball and the Grasshopper's Feast;
The Trumpeter, Gadfly, has summoned the crew,
And the Revels are now only waiting for you."
So said little Robert, and pacing along,
His merry Companions came forth in a throng,
And on the smooth Grass by the side of a Wood,
Beneath a broad Oak that for ages had stood,
Saw the Children of Earth and the Tenants of Air
For an Evening's Amusement together repair.

And there came the Beetle, so blind and so black,
Who carried the Emmet, his friend, on his back.
And there was the Gnat and the Dragonfly too,
With all their Relations, green, orange, and blue.
And there came the Moth, with his plumage of down,
And the Hornet in jacket of yellow and brown;
Who with him the Wasp, his companion, did bring,
But they promised that evening to lay by their sting.
And the sly little Dormouse crept out of his hole,
And brought to the Feast his blind brother, the Mole.
And the Snail, with his horns peeping out of his shell
Came from a great distance, the length of an ell.

A Mushroom their Table, and on it was laid
A water-dock leaf, which a table-cloth made.
The Viands were various, to each of their taste,
And the Bee brought her honey to crown the Repast.
Then close on his haunches, so solemn and wise,
The Frog from a corner looked up to the skies;
And the Squirrel, well pleased such diversions to see,
Mounted high overhead and looked down from a tree.

Then out came the Spider, with fingers so fine,
To show his dexterity on the tight-line.
From one branch to another his cobwebs he slung,
Then quick as an arrow he darted along.
But just in the middle—oh! shocking to tell,
From his rope, in an instant, poor Harlequin fell.
Yet he touched not the ground, but with talons outspread,
Hung suspended in air, at the end of a thread.

Then the Grasshopper came with a jerk and a spring,
Very long was his Leg, though but short was his Wing;
He took but three leaps, and was soon out of sight,
Then chirped his own praises the rest of the night.
With step so majestic the Snail did advance;
And promised the Gazers a Minuet to dance;
But they all laughed so loud that he pulled in his head,
And went in his own little chamber to bed.
Then as Evening gave way to the shadows of Night,
Their Watchman, the Glowworm, came out with a light.

"Then home let us hasten, while yet we can see,
For no Watchman is waiting for you and for me."
So said little Robert, and pacing along,
His merry Companions returned in a throng.

WILLIAM ROSCOE

DANCING ON THE HILLTOPS

Dancing on the hilltops,
  Singing in the valleys,
Laughing with the echoes,
  Merry little Alice.

Playing games with lambkins
  In the flowering valley,
Gathering pretty posies,
  Helpful little Alice.

If her father's cottage
  Turned into a palace,
And he owned the hilltops
  And the flowering valleys,
She'd be none the happier,
  Happy little Alice.

CHRISTINA ROSSETTI

PICTURE BOOKS IN WINTER

Summer fading, winter comes—
Frosty mornings, tingling thumbs,
Window robins, winter rooks,
And the picture storybooks.

Water now is turned to stone
Nurse and I can walk upon;
Still we find the flowing brooks
In the picture storybooks.

All the pretty things put by,
Wait upon the children's eye,
Sheep and shepherds, trees and crooks
In the picture storybooks.

We may see how all things are,
Seas and cities, near and far,
And the flying fairies' looks,
In the picture storybooks.

How am I to sing your praise,
Happy chimney-corner days,
Sitting safe in nursery nooks,
Reading picture storybooks?

ROBERT LOUIS STEVENSON

GAY GO UP AND GAY GO DOWN

Gay go up and gay go down,
To ring the bells of London Town.

Bull's eyes and targets,
Say the bells of St. Margaret's.

Brickbats and tiles,
Say the bells of St. Giles'.

Halfpence and farthings,
Say the bells of St. Martin's.

Oranges and lemons,
Say the bells of St. Clement's.

Pancakes and fritters,
Say the bells of St. Peter's.

Two sticks and an apple,
Say the bells at Whitechapel.

Old Father Baldpate,
Say the slow bells at Aldgate.

Pokers and tongs,
Say the bells of St. John's.

Kettles and pans,
Say the bells of St. Anne's.

You owe me ten shillings,
Say the Bells of St. Helen's.

When will you pay me?
Say the bells at Old Bailey.

When I grow rich,
Say the bells at Shoreditch.

Pray when will that be?
Say the bells of Stepney.

I am sure I don't know,
Says the great bell at Bow.

MOTHER GOOSE RHYME

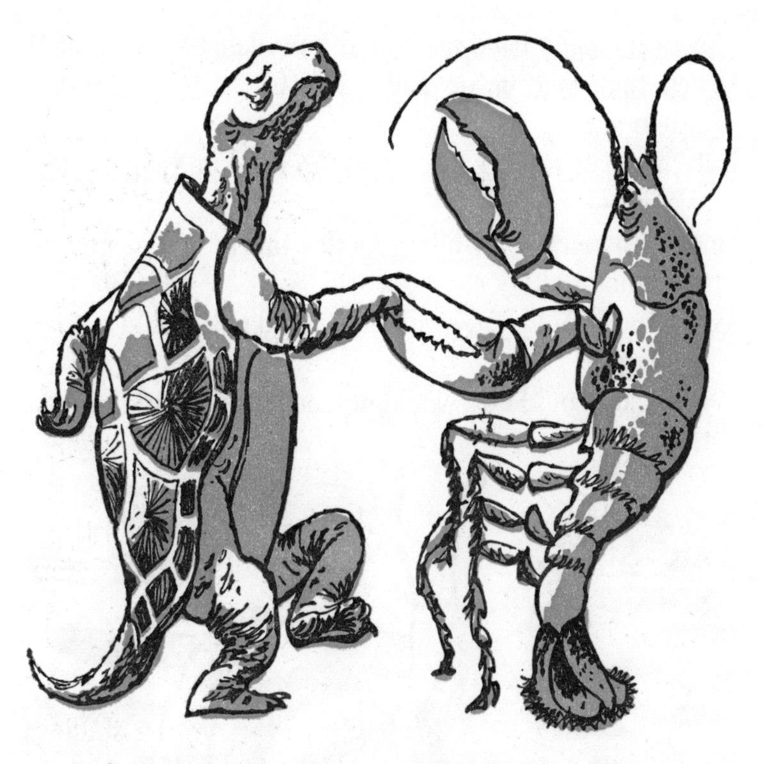

THE LOBSTER QUADRILLE

"Will you walk a little faster?" said a whiting to a snail,
"There's a porpoise close behind us, and he's treading on my tail.
See how eagerly the lobsters and the turtles all advance!
They are waiting on the shingle—will you come and join the dance?
Will you, won't you, will you, won't you, will you join the dance?
Will you, won't you, will you, won't you, won't you join the dance?

"You can really have no notion how delightful it will be
When they take us up and throw us, with the lobsters, out to sea!"
But the snail replied "Too far, too far!" and gave a look askance–
Said he thanked the whiting kindly, but he would not join the dance.
Would not, could not, would not, could not, would not join the dance.
Would not, could not, would not, could not, could not join the dance.

"What matters it how far we go?" his scaly friend replied,
"There is another shore, you know, upon the other side.
The further off from England the nearer is to France—
Then turn not pale, beloved snail, but come and join the
  dance.
Will you, won't you, will you, won't you, will you join the
  dance?
Will you, won't you, will you, won't you, won't you join the
  dance?"

LEWIS CARROLL

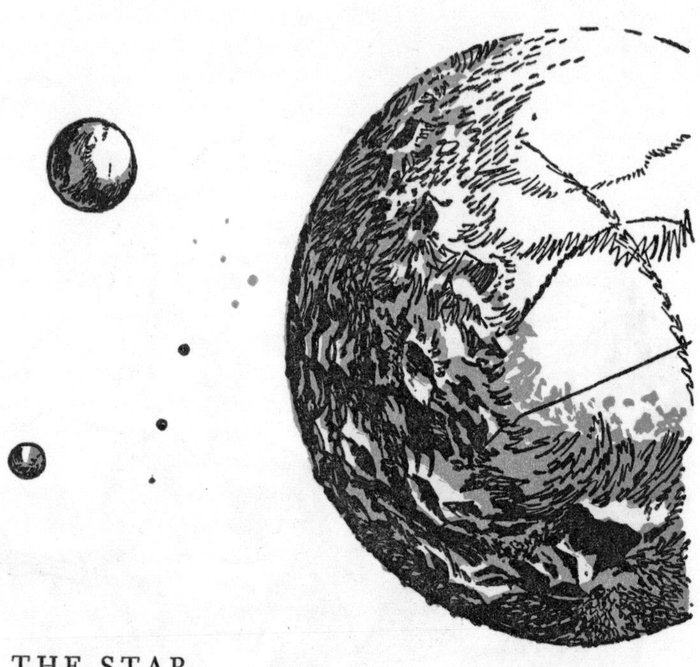

THE STAR

Twinkle, twinkle, little star,
How I wonder what you are,
Up above the world so high,
Like a diamond in the sky.

When the blazing sun is set,
And the grass with dew is wet,
Then you show your little light,
Twinkle, twinkle, all the night.

Then the traveler in the dark,
Thanks you for your tiny spark,
He could not see where to go,
If you did not twinkle so.

In the dark blue sky you keep,
And often through my curtains peep,
For you never shut your eye,
Till the sun is in the sky.

As your bright and tiny spark,
Lights the traveler in the dark,
Though I know not what you are,
Twinkle, twinkle, little star.

JANE TAYLOR

AMERICA THE BEAUTIFUL

O beautiful for spacious skies,
For amber waves of grain,
For purple mountain majesties
Above the fruited plain!
America! America!
God shed His grace on thee,
And crown thy good with brotherhood
From sea to shining sea!

O beautiful for pilgrim feet,
Whose stern, impassioned stress
A thoroughfare for freedom beat
Across the wilderness!
America! America!
God mend thine every flaw,
Confirm thy soul in self-control,
Thy liberty in law!

O beautiful for heroes proved
In liberating strife,
Who more than self their country loved,
And mercy more than life!
America! America!
May God thy gold refine
Till all success be nobleness
And every gain divine!

O beautiful for patriot dream
That sees beyond the years
Thine alabaster cities gleam
Undimmed by human tears!
America! America!
God shed His grace on thee
And crown thy good with brotherhood
From sea to shining sea!

KATHARINE LEE BATES

RAIN IN SUMMER

How beautiful is the rain!
After the dust and heat,
In the broad and fiery street,
In the narrow lane,
How beautiful is the rain!

How it clatters along the roofs
Like the tramp of hoofs!
How it gushes and struggles out
From the throat of the overflowing spout!
Across the window-pane
It pours and pours;
And swift and wide,
With a muddy tide,
Like a river down the gutter roars
The rain, the welcome rain!

HENRY WADSWORTH LONGFELLOW

What Eddie Brought Home

by CAROLYN HAYWOOD

illustrated by
EZRA JACK KEATS

Little Eddie was the youngest of the four Wilson boys. There was Rudy, aged twelve, the twins, Joe and Frank, who were nine, and Eddie. Eddie was seven.

There were a number of boys and girls in the neighborhood with whom the older boys played, but there were none the same age as Eddie. The older boys were always telling him that he was too little to be in their gang, but this never discouraged Eddie. He just hung around and found ways to get in on nearly everything the older boys did. But sometimes he had to think fast and work hard to do it.

Of all the girls in the neighborhood, he liked Betsy best. If the boys went off without him, he could go over to Betsy's. Betsy was always glad to see him. Usually, they played checkers.

Little Eddie was very fond of animals. He brought all of the stray animals home with him. Stray cats, stray dogs, birds

that had fallen out of their nests, turtles, snails, garter snakes; anything that was alive, Eddie brought home with him. He was always getting fish heads from the fish market for the cats, saving bones for dogs, catching flies for turtles, and putting snails and garter snakes in boxes. His mother complained that every stray cat for miles around could smell the fish heads, and that they all made tracks for the Wilsons' back door; that every dog in the neighborhood knew Eddie's address and that he was always good for a bone. His father said if Eddie brought home another turtle, he would make soup out of it. But none of this discouraged Eddie. He didn't think that the complaining done by his mother and father meant anything.

Eddie had another deep interest. It was in all kinds of signs. He simply loved signs, and every time he saw one he

would make one just like it. His bedroom was filled with signs. When you opened Eddie's door, you read, *Stop, Look and Listen, Silence, Men Working, Slow, Danger, Road Under Construction.*

Eddie also brought home junk of all kinds. Every wastepaper basket was hidden treasure to Eddie; when the housecleaning season came around, Eddie could hardly stay in school, he was so afraid he would miss something that was being put out for the rubbish collection.

One corner of the workshop in the basement was supposed to be Eddie's private corner where he could keep his junk. Of course, Eddie didn't call it junk. He called it his valuable property. He had old radio parts, ear phones, old tubes, and dials. Once he came home with an old phonograph horn almost as big as himself. When Eddie left the house, the family had no idea what he would bring back with him. His mother often said that nothing would surprise her. But the day came when she was more than surprised. It was the day Eddie brought home a telegraph pole.

One day Eddie came home with an old filing case which he had found sitting on top of a trash barrel. His bedroom was his office from then on, and he decided he must have a desk. When his father remarked one evening that he was getting a new desk, Eddie piped up, "Can I have the old one, Papa?"

"Nothing doing!" said Rudy. "I'm the oldest. I'm the one that needs the desk."

"No! No!" cried the twins in one breath.

"We get the desk! Don't we, Daddy?" Frank added.

"It was Grandfather's desk," said Joe.

"And we were named after Grandfather," said Frank.

"I ought to chop it up for firewood," said their father. "There isn't a stick of wood left and I can't find any place to buy any. And it's only February. We'll need wood until April."

"Oh, Daddy!" cried Rudy. "You wouldn't burn up Grandfather's desk, would you?"

"I didn't say I would," said his father. "I said I should."

"But you won't, will you, Pop?" said Eddie.

"No, I won't," he replied. "But I'll tell you what I will do. I'll give the desk to whichever one of you boys brings in the most wood."

"Oh, Dad!" said Rudy. "Where are we going to get any wood?"

"I don't know," said Father. "But I have tried, and I can't see any reason why you boys shouldn't try. Is it a bargain?"

"Okay," said Rudy.

"Okay," said the twins.

"Okay," said Eddie.

Several weeks passed, and the twins didn't give the wood a thought. They were too busy playing ice hockey to think of wood, and then, one day, Eddie came home with the telegraph pole. It came about in this way.

One afternoon when Eddie came home from school, he found the men from the telegraph company replacing the telegraph pole that stood at the corner of the street on which Eddie lived. Eddie was thrilled. He sat down on the curb on the opposite side of the street and watched every move that the men made. Once he called out, "Would you like to have me help you?"

The man nearest Eddie looked up. "No, thanks," he said. "I think we'll be able to do it all by ourselves. You just stay where you are and rest yourself."

Eddie watched the men handle the ropes and he saw the new pole slide into place. Then he looked at the old pole lying in the street. "I certainly would like to have that pole," thought Eddie. "That pole is certainly super." He watched the men as they got ready to move the old pole. Suddenly

Eddie said, "If you don't want that pole, I would like to have it."

The men looked at Eddie in surprise. "Now what do you

want with a telegraph pole?" the foreman asked.

"Well, my father could use it," said Eddie. "We've been having a hard time to get wood for our fireplace."

"I'm afraid your father will have to get his wood some place else," said the foreman.

"But my father said if I could get him some wood, he would give me my grandfather's desk," said Eddie.

"He did?" said the foreman. Then he looked at the other men. "How about it, fellows? Does the kid get his grand-pop's desk?"

"Sure," said one of the men. "Here, sonny! Help your-self to Grandpop's desk."

"Oh, thanks!" said Eddie. Then he added, "I live right up the street in that white house with the white fence. Could you help me carry it home?"

The men laughed. "Help you carry it home, hey?" said one. "Well, fellas, shall we help the big boy carry the little telegraph pole home?"

The five men picked up the telegraph pole and Eddie put his arm around the center of it. Then they all marched up the street, through Eddie's front gate, and put the pole down in the front yard.

"Now I suppose you want us to help you cut it up," said the foreman.

"Oh, no, that's all right," said Eddie. "My father will cut it up."

When Mrs. Wilson came home, she found Eddie sitting on the telegraph pole. "Look, Mother!" he said. "I got the wood for Papa."

"Eddie! Where did you get that!" exclaimed his mother.

"The telegraph men gave it to me," replied Eddie. "Now I'll get Granddad's desk."

"I guess you will," laughed Mrs. Wilson.

When the other boys came home, they were surprised to see the telegraph pole, and when his father heard of how

Eddie came home with the telegraph pole, his glasses fell off, right into his bowl of soup.

The day Grandfather's desk was placed in Eddie's room, Eddie put a sign on his door. It said, *Men Working.*

The family, who were downstairs, could hear Eddie scrambling around his room like a squirrel in the attic. They knew what he was doing. He was arranging his office. Then, after a while, his mother noticed that everything was very quiet in Eddie's room. She went to his door and gently opened it. When she looked in, there was little Eddie, with his head on Grandfather's desk, sound asleep. Standing on the desk, and showing above his head, was a sign which said, *Help Wanted.*

His mother called downstairs to his father. Father came upstairs. He picked up Eddie and laid him gently on his bed. His mother undressed him and tucked him under the covers. Through all of this Eddie slept.

As Mother was leaving the room, she saw another sign. She picked it up and hung it on the bed post at the head of Eddie's bed. It said, *Do Not Disturb.*

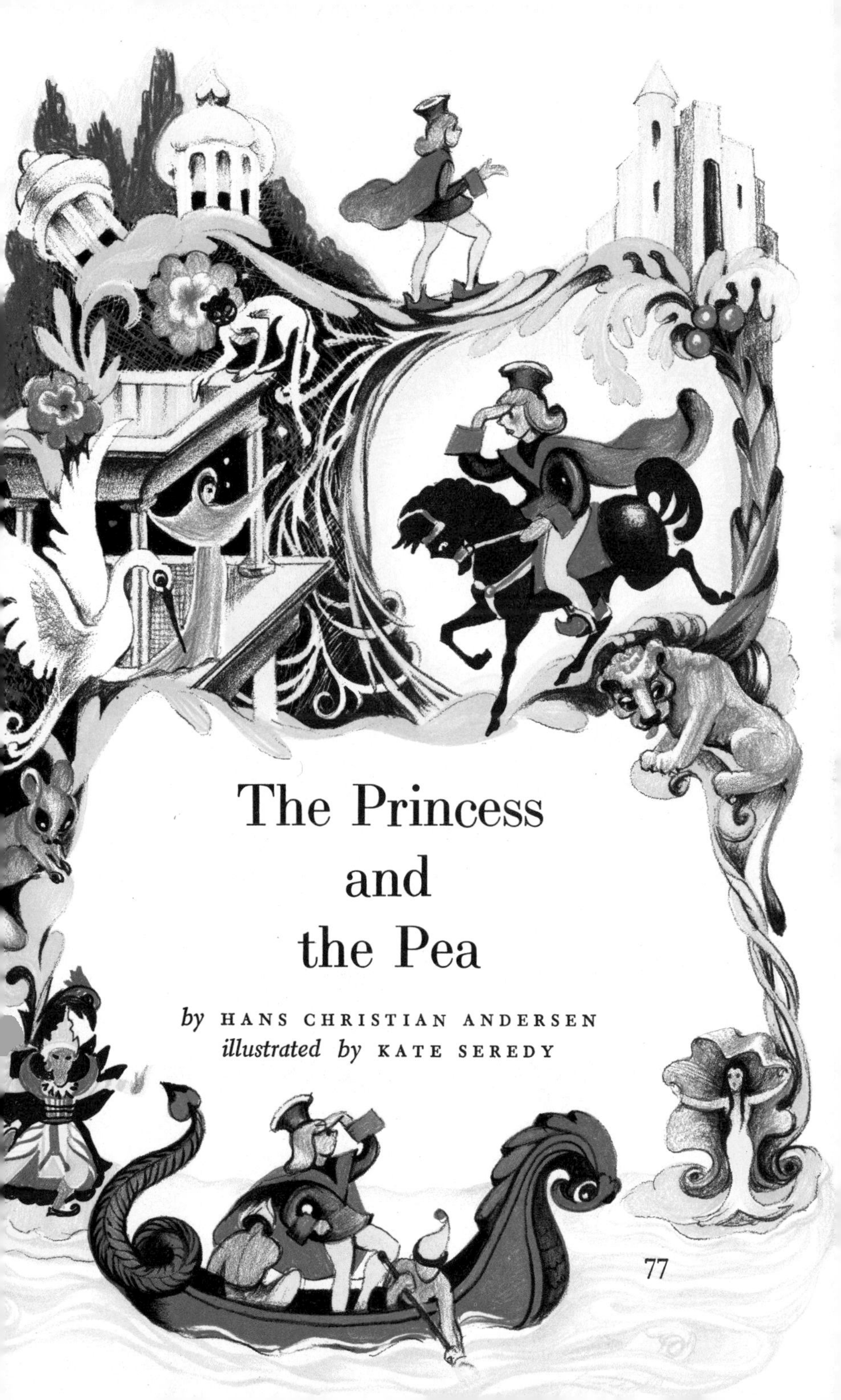

The Princess and the Pea

by HANS CHRISTIAN ANDERSEN
illustrated by KATE SEREDY

Egypt
France
Babylon
India

There was once a Prince who wished to marry a Princess; but then she must be a real Princess. He traveled all over the world in hopes of finding such a lady; but there was al-

ways something wrong. Princesses he found in plenty; but whether they were real Princesses it was impossible for him to decide, for now one thing, now another, seemed to him not quite right about the ladies. At last he returned to his palace quite cast down, because he wished so much to have a real Princess for his wife.

One evening a fearful tempest arose; it thundered and lightened, and the rain poured down from the sky in torrents; besides, it was as dark as pitch. All at once there was

heard a violent knocking at the door, and the old King, the Prince's father, went out himself to open it.

It was a Princess who was standing outside the door. What with the rain and the wind, she was in a sad condition. The water trickled down from her hair, and her clothes clung to her body. She said she was a real Princess.

"Ah! we shall soon see that!" thought the old Queen-mother. However, she said not a word of what she was going to do; but went into the bedroom, took all the bedclothes off the bed, and put three little peas on the bedstead. She then laid twenty mattresses one upon another over the three peas, and put twenty feather beds over the mattresses.

Upon this bed the Princess was to pass the night.

The next morning she was asked how she had slept. “Oh, very badly indeed!” she replied. “I have scarcely closed my eyes the whole night through. I do not know what was in my bed, but I had something hard under me, and am all over black and blue. It has hurt me so much!”

Now it was plain that the lady must be a real Princess, since she had been able to feel the three little peas through twenty mattresses and twenty feather beds. None but a real Princess could have had such a delicate sense of feeling.

The Prince accordingly made her his wife, being now convinced that he had found a real Princess. The three peas were, however, put into the cabinet of curiosities, where they are still to be seen, provided they are not lost.

Wasn't this a lady of real delicacy?

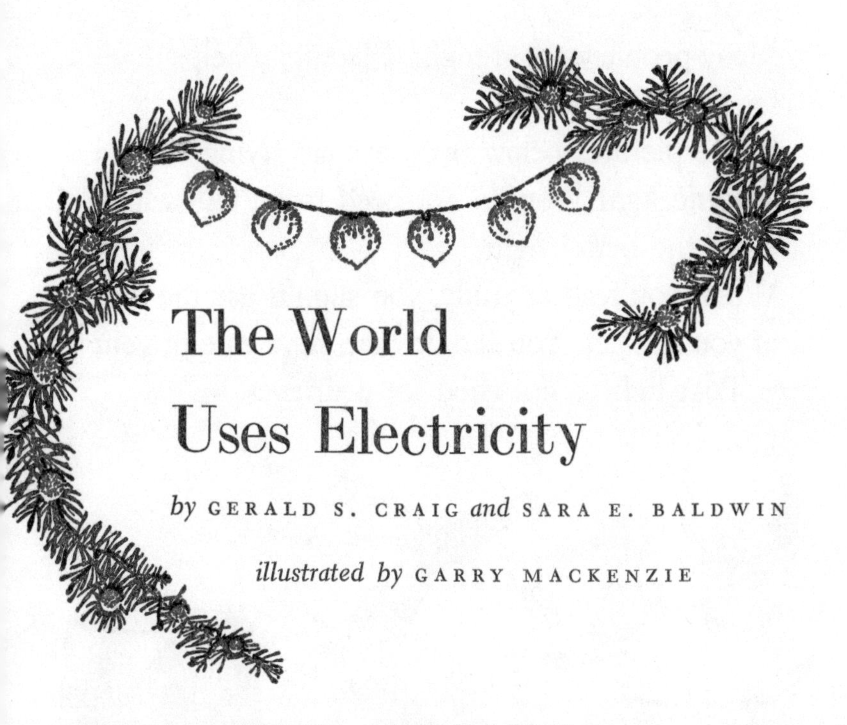

The World Uses Electricity

by GERALD S. CRAIG *and* SARA E. BALDWIN

illustrated by GARRY MACKENZIE

ELECTRICITY GIVES LIGHT

All through the day and all through the night, electricity works for you.

Try to count the ways that electricity helps you. How many ways there are! Do you think you can count all of them?

At night city streets are bright with light. You hardly know it is night until you look up at the dark sky. All over the city people are using electric lights.

Many people work at night. Electricity helps them to see to do their work.

In the pictures below two boys are trying to read by electric light. You do not need to be told which boy has the better light.

When you read or study, you should use the best light you can get. You should take good care of your eyes. Poor light is not good for your eyes.

Many machines are run by electricity. Some of them are in people's homes. How many can you see in the picture? These machines help to make housework easy.

Many, many of the things people use every day are made in factories. Shoes, caps, dresses, suits, coats, leggings, chairs, beds, tables, dishes——hundreds of things are made in factories. In many of these factories, the machines are run by electricity.

Fred lives in the city. Wherever he goes, electricity helps him to travel. An electric elevator takes him from his apartment to the street floor. An electric elevator takes him up and down in the big city buildings.

Sometimes Fred rides downtown on an electric bus. When he goes to visit his grandmother he rides on an electric train.

Electricity helps people on farms, too. Everyone in the Davis family is glad electricity has come to their farm.

Mrs. Davis says, "Housework is much easier now that the electric pump sends water into the house."

The pump sends water to the barnyard. Peter says, "The pump makes it easier to water the cows and chickens."

Mr. Davis says, "The electric milking machine is wonderful. It milks all the cows in a very short time."

In the city and in the country, in factories and on farms, electricity helps people with their work.

By radio we learn what people are doing in all parts of the world. Some radio talks come to us from far, far away. But we hear the words as soon as they are said.

The telephone carries words as fast as the radio. How quickly your mother can talk with her friends in any part of town! How quickly she can call help when someone is hurt! How easily your father can talk with other men at work!

Over the ocean, across the land, around the world, words go traveling. Electricity sends them on their way.

Before people had telephones to use, they sent messages by telegraph. People today send messages by telegraph. This is a quick way to send a message.

The man in the picture on this page is sending a telegraph message. Electricity sends these messages on their way.

News from faraway places is sent us by telegraph, telephone, radio, and television. Words travel far and fast because we know how to use electricity. Without electricity, we might wait for days, weeks, or even years for news to reach us.

ELECTRICITY COMES TO YOUR TOWN

It is night. Bob comes into a dark room. He pushes the button on the wall. At once the dark room is almost as light as day. Electricity has gone into the electric bulbs.

Bob's mother turns a button on the electric stove. Soon the burner on top of the stove is hot. Electricity has gone into the stove.

How does electricity get into a house?

Electricity does not stay in the wall. It is not waiting there for someone to push the button.

Electricity comes to homes from far away. It is sent

out from a powerhouse. Big machines are in the powerhouse. These machines send out electric power for people to use.

Great wires go out from the powerhouse. Electric power goes along these wires. The great wires take electric power to cities and farms. They take the electric power that helps the people to live better. The wires take electric power to your town.

Wires go along the streets of your town. They may go under the street. In some towns you cannot see these wires. They are not in anyone's way when they are under the street.

Smaller wires go from the street into the houses. Wires go to all the rooms of the houses. Electricity goes through these wires. You push the button. Electricity comes to do its work.

NO ONE SEES ELECTRICITY

All around you electricity is at work. You see what it does, but no one ever has seen electricity itself.

You cannot see electricity as it travels along a wire. If you could see inside the wire, you could not see electricity there.

No one sees electricity as it goes out from the powerhouse. No one sees the electricity in a light bulb or an electric iron. You just see what electricity does. You see the light which electricity makes in the bulb. You feel the heat in the iron or the stove.

ELECTRICITY AT WORK

Not all electricity is sent out from a powerhouse. You can get electricity in other ways. One of these ways is to use a dry cell.

If you have a dry cell, you can watch electricity at work. You can make a bell ring. Find the picture of a dry cell at the top of the page. Do you see the two posts on the top?

Now find the picture of an electric bell. Do you see the posts under the box on the bell?

You will use all of these posts when you make the bell ring. Now you are ready to watch electricity at work.

Fasten the end of one wire around one post of the dry cell. Fasten the other end of the wire around one post on the bell.

Take the other wire. Fasten it to the other post of the dry cell and the other post of the bell.

Does the bell begin to ring? Does it ring and ring?

How can you make the bell stop ringing? Just take one end of one of the wires away from the post. Then the bell cannot ring.

ELECTRICITY TRAVELS ALONG A PATHWAY

Electricity travels. It travels from the powerhouse to you.

It travels from the dry cell to the bell and makes it ring.

How does electricity travel? It goes along a pathway. You can find a pathway for electricity.

Look at the picture. Do you see the path which electricity takes?

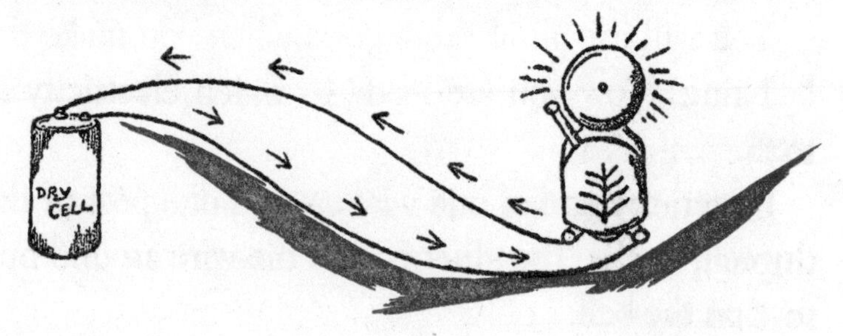

Electricity goes to the bell through the wires. It must go to the bell along one wire. It must come back to the dry cell along the other wire.

Electricity goes around and around on its pathway. It always comes back to the place from which it started.

An electric bell will ring because the electricity has a pathway. The wires, the cell, and the bell make a pathway for the electricity.

Take off one of the wires that go from the dry cell to the bell. It will look like the picture.

Now the bell will not ring. Something has happened to the pathway.

Electricity cannot go from the end of the wire through the air to the bell. The wires must be fastened so that they make a pathway for electricity.

ELECTRICITY AND GOOD TIMES

It is night, but the people in the picture can see to swim very well.

Electric lights help many people to play out-of-doors at night. Have you ever watched people playing out-of-doors at night? What were they playing?

Electricity helps many people to have a good time.

Have you ever had a ride on a merry-go-round?

Do you like to go to a moving picture show? Moving picture machines are run by electricity.

Have you played with an electric train? Have you played with other toys that are run by electricity? Electricity helps you to have fun in many ways.

USE ELECTRICITY WITH CARE

Always turn off electricity as soon as you have finished using it.

Never turn on electricity when your hands are wet.

Never turn on electricity when you are touching water in any way.

Be careful of electric lights. Never put your hand into the place where the light bulb goes. Never put anything into the place where the electricity comes out.

Sometimes you may see long wires in the street. Keep away from them. Never touch them. They may be electric wires.

The True Book of the Circus

by MABEL HARMER

illustrated by PAUL GALDONE

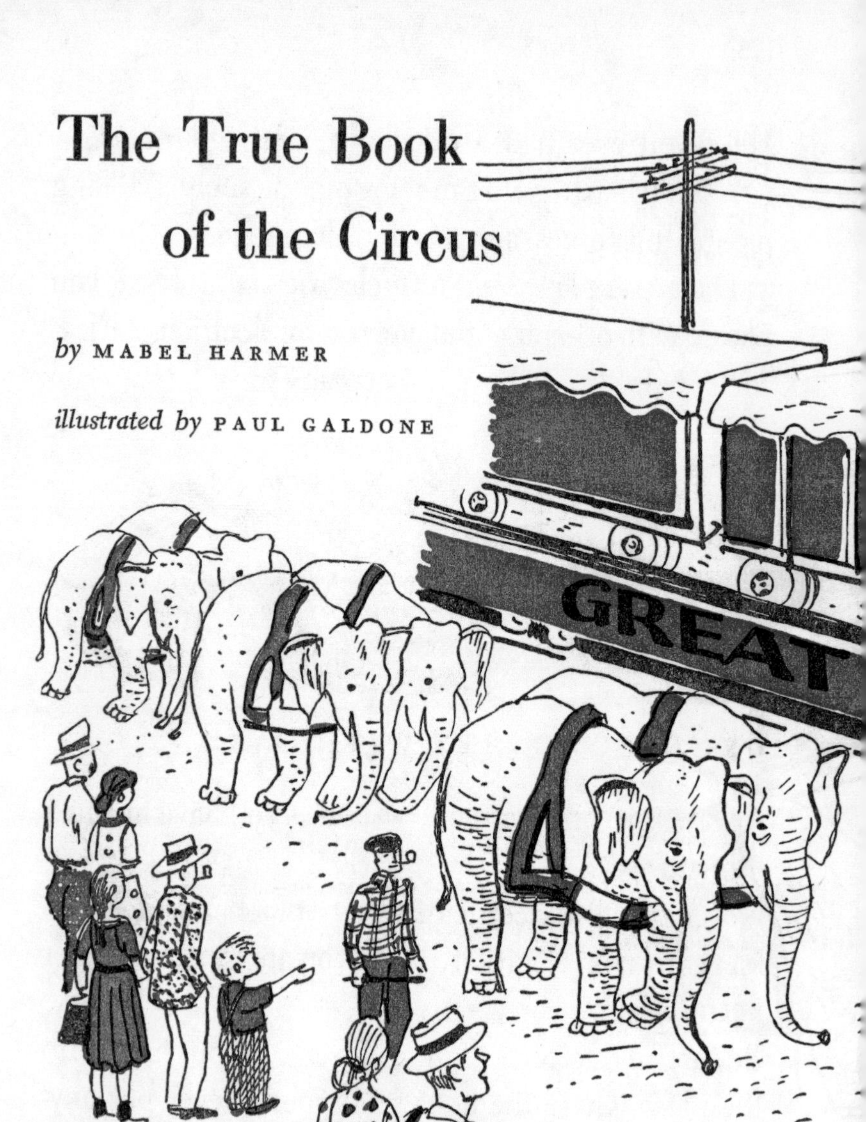

A circus moves from town to town.
A big circus moves in its own gay trains.

The men who put up the tents ride in the first train.
Tents, seats, wooden stands come in the next two trains.
The people who are in the show, and the animals, ride in the last train.
The circus people sleep on the train.
Each one has his own bed and a small closet.
The trains arrive early in the morning.

Trucks take the tents to the circus lot.
The Cook House is the first tent to go up.
Meals are served in the Cook House.
A yellow flag tells when meals are ready.

CIRC

Then the animal tents go up.
They must be ready when the animals come.
Elephants, camels, zebras, and horses walk from the train.

Wild animals ride in red wagons.
Lions, tigers and leopards are called "cats."
The lion is the most easily trained.
The tiger can learn more tricks than a lion, but it is more dangerous.
The leopard is the most dangerous of all.

There are two kinds of circus horses.

The "baggage stock" pulls the wagons.

The "ring stock" performs in the show.

Sometimes the elephants help with the work.
They work very hard when it is muddy.

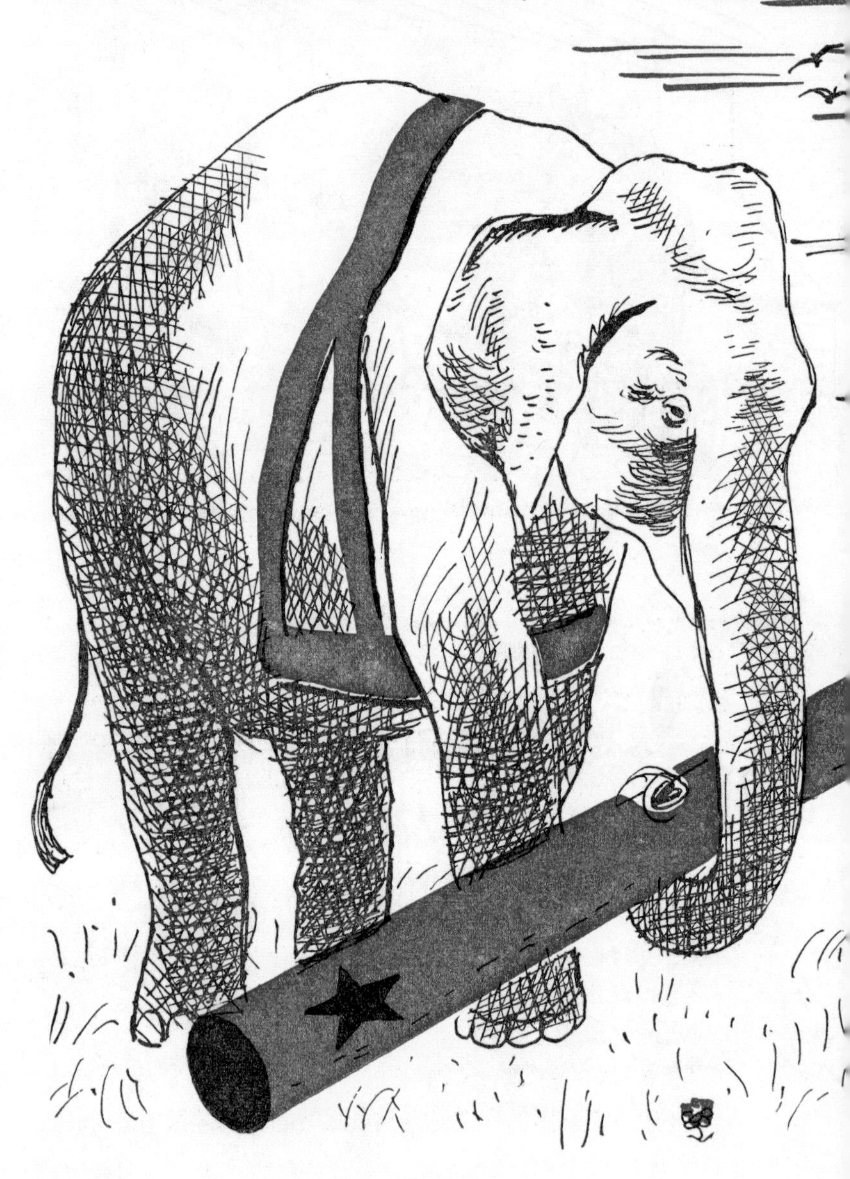

The Big Top is the last tent to go up.
Here the show will take place.
Seats are put in place.
"Tight rope" wires are strung.
Lights are put in. The circus city is built.
Miles of rope are used by a circus.
New rope is used each year.
Good strong rope helps keep performers safe.

The animals are the first to get breakfast.
Elephants, horses and zebras get hay.
The "cats" get meat.

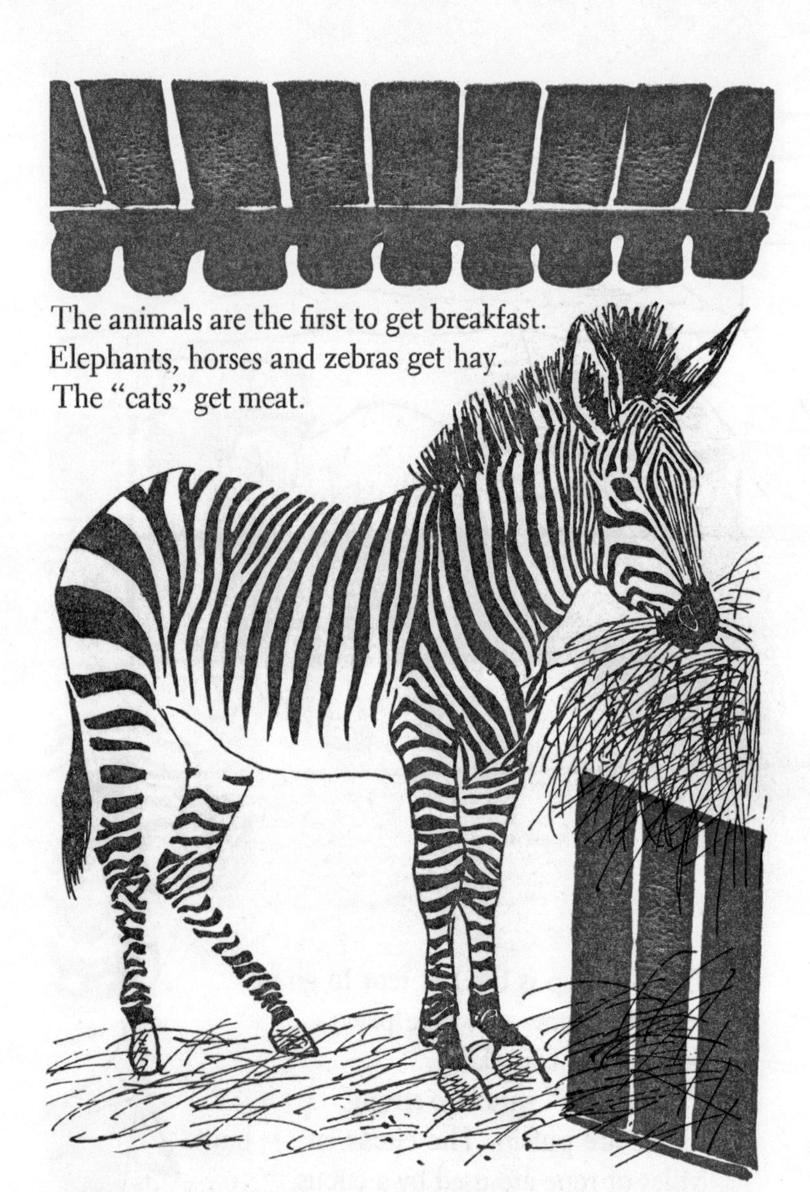

All of the animals get plenty of water.
There is fish for the seals.

There is fruit for the apes and monkeys.
The flag goes up on the Cook House.
The circus people have their breakfast.

At last it is time for the show.

The band plays a lively tune. This is the clock of the circus. The music tells the performers how much time they have for each act.

The show opens with a big parade.
The big show goes on.
The performers wait their turn outside the tent.

Between shows the stands are swept.
Seats are dusted. Papers are picked up.
The show people rest in the "back yard" of the circus.
Some wash, iron, or read.
Some learn new tricks.
Each person has a bucket with his name on it.
It is his bathtub.

A circus doctor tries to keep the animals well. He takes care of the sick ones.

Trainers oil the elephants' tender skin. They trim the elephants' toenails.

In the fall the circus goes to its winter home.
New tents are made.
Old tents are fixed.
Everything gets a fresh coat of paint.

Birds of the South Pacific

A.M.N.H.—Armand Denis Exp.

NEW GUINEA HORNBILL

Photographs from The American Museum of Natural History—Armand Denis Expedition, where so credited. Other photographs by E. Thomas Gilliard.

A.M.N.H.—Armand Denis Exp.

NEW GUINEA BARRED RAIL

New Guinea, in the South Pacific Ocean, is the center of a group of nearly 500 islands. Dense jungles, deep swamps and countless rivers make them a tropical wonderland. Some of the mountains are three miles high. And many of the birds that live there are found nowhere else in the world.

One of these feathered marvels is the New Guinea Hornbill. This is a big one, as you can tell from the picture. This bird is well named, too, for that great bill does look like a horn. The one in the photograph is a female, and she lays her eggs in a tree hole. When she begins to sit on them, her mate plugs up the hole with mud so that she has to stay there until some time after they hatch. Meanwhile he feeds her through a narrow slot which he has left open for this purpose. When the young birds are ready to leave, the wall is broken and mother and her brood fly away. A hornbill's flight is noisy and sounds like hissing steam.

Hornbills spend most of their time in trees. But the New Guinea Barred Rail lives entirely on the ground. His home is in swamps and grasslands among the mountains. There he skulks through the undergrowth on his long-toed feet looking for his favorite worm and insect food. These

WHITE-NECKED HERON

rails are hard to find, for they would rather run away than fly up into the air where they could be seen.

New Guinea has many kinds of long-legged wading birds, such as the White-necked Heron. These herons walk around very slowly in shallow water until they get close to a fish or a frog. Then they suddenly shoot out their long necks and snatch the prey with that spear-like bill. The bird in the picture has his neck folded back on his shoulders.

Owls and Honey-Eaters

In New Guinea and many of its nearby islands there are numerous kinds of owls. Most of these good-sized birds do their food-hunting at night. Their eyes are specially built to see in the dark, and their feathers have such soft edges that the flapping of their wings makes no sound at all. The result is that they can snatch up a mouse or rat before he suspects that an enemy is anywhere in the neighborhood. All owls

A.M.N.H.—Armand Denis Exp.

PAPUAN FROGMOUTH

A.M.N.H.—Armand Denis Exp.

BLACK BARN OWL

A.M.N.H.—Armand Denis Exp.

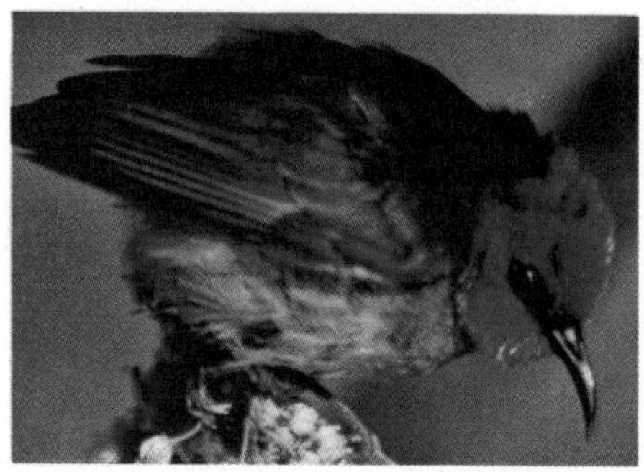

ADOLPH'S HONEY-EATER

have very strong feet and sharp talons, so their victims seldom escape.

Honey-eaters are entirely different from owls. They are much smaller, and they have long, hollow tongues with which they suck in the nectar produced by flowers. These tongues have brush-like tips which are useful for catching small insects and spiders. Their bills, too, are very sharp-pointed. Sometimes they are curved so that they can reach into tiny crevices in tree bark where tasty little bugs may be hiding. This whole tongue and bill arrangement is a good deal like that of our North American hummingbirds.

Most of the honey-eaters are rather plain in color. But a few kinds, like the red-headed Adolph's, are quite showy.

Some Believe-It-or-Not Birds

All kinds of pigeons build flimsy nests. But the green, white-headed Magnificent Fruit Pigeon chooses a location that is flimsy, too. A favorite place is on the flat tops of palm leaves. When strong winds blow, the parent bird has a hard time keeping her two white eggs from tumbling to the ground and breaking to bits.

MAGNIFICENT FRUIT PIGEON

Paradise Flycatchers are found in the deep forests on

A.M.N.H.—Armand Denis Exp.

PARADISE FLYCATCHER

BLACK-CAPPED LORY

LESSER BIRD OF PARADISE

A.M.N.H.—Armand Denis Exp.

MACGREGOR'S BOWER-BIRD

all of the New Guinea islands. They catch thousands of insects in their wide, yellow-throated mouths. Those long bristles at the sides of the open beak help to trap a flying insect if he tries to escape.

Many kinds of parrots, too, live in these tropical woods. One of the most plentiful of them is the Black-capped Lory. He feeds on flower nectar and fruit. When his strong beak has opened up the blossom or fruit, his tongue goes to work. It has a brush-like tip for picking up the sweet liquid and any insects that may be in it.

A male Lesser Bird of Paradise is probably the most gorgeous forest bird on the South Pacific islands. He loves to show off his fantastic plumage by spreading his tail and wings and ruffling the feathers on his neck and head. While doing this he caws and "wucks" as if he wanted to make everybody look at him. It is a strange fact that no one has ever found out where these amazing birds build their nests, even though professional hunters used to collect and sell their plumes.

The nest of MacGregor's Gardener Bower-Bird, however, is well known. It is a firm, basket-like home made of small vines, sticks and leaves. And it is always built in the mountain forests of New Guinea, where there are over a hundred peaks 10,000 feet high.

Most of the nineteen known kinds of bower-birds have long, unbelievably romantic courtships. In some cases the male builds a stick house or "bower" several feet high. Then he constructs a "garden" of bright seeds, colored leaves, shells and flowers around it. But the MacGregor's bower is always made around a sapling growing in the center of a yard-wide saucer of green moss. When he has finished it, the bird keeps this moss carpet completely free of even the smallest twig or fallen leaf scrap.

Another believe–it–or–not bird is the beautiful, but stupid, Crowned Pigeon. He is as big as a small turkey, and his great feather crest looks almost like blue and white lace. Sometimes you see quite a flock of these strange birds feeding on or near the ground in a lowland forest.

A few of the largest New Guinea birds have completely lost the power of flight. Their wings are no more than stubs. The only way they can get around is on foot. One of

A.M.N.H.—Armand Denis Exp.

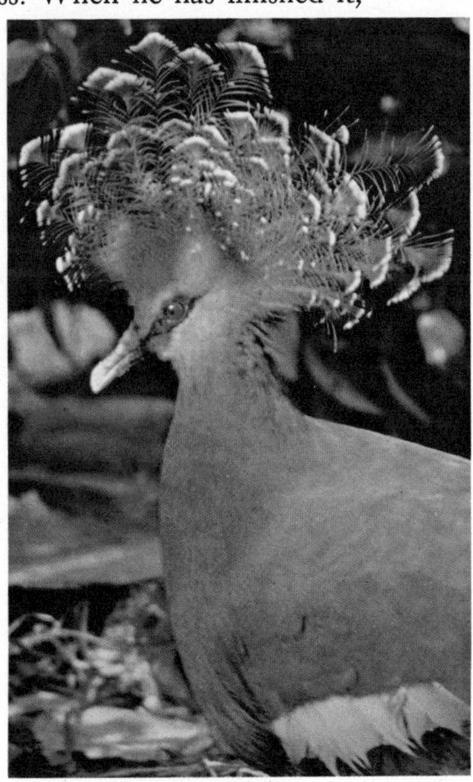

CROWNED PIGEON

these peculiar creatures is the Swamp Hen. He lives in marshes and along river banks, where he eats grasshoppers, small lizards, frogs and pieces of plants. He can swim splendidly, and night is his favorite time for roaming and for searching for food. The New Guinea Swamp Hen is a colorful bird, with scarlet bill, scarlet iris and bald scarlet pate. This, combined with his habit of climbing to high points to peer out inquisitively, makes him an easy bird to see.

SWAMP HEN OR GIANT GALLINULE

The Book of Nah-wee

by GRACE *and* CARL MOON

illustrated by PAUL LANTZ

Nah-wee was a little Indian girl. She lived high on a big flat hill on the very edge of the desert. Nah-wee was very small and very fat and her eyes were round and black as buttons.

She was dressed like a very little old woman, with a long dress that came almost to the ground, and a red sash wound around and around her waist, and dangly blue earrings in her ears. But Nah-wee did not feel like a woman, and never did Nah-wee *act* like a woman at all, you shall see!

Dat-say was a boy. He was small too, but when he was with Nah-wee he felt very big and strong. Nah-wee and Dat-say lived in the same town (called a pueblo), and they were friends. They had very good times together, and I am going to tell you about some of those good times.

THE HUNGRY DOG

One bright and shiny morning Dat-say came to Nah-wee and said, "My mother has a need for some grasses and reeds to make baskets and I know a very good place to go and find them. Will you come, too?" And Nah-wee jumped up from the floor where she had been sitting and a dance-feeling came into her feet and a shiny look into her eyes, and Dat-say knew that she was very glad to go. He had food that his mother had given him, piki bread made of corn, and dried apricots, and a little piece of dried goat's meat, and he knew of a place where they could get water from a spring. So they started out right away.

First they had to go down the steep trail that led from the top of the flat-topped hill—hills like that are called mesas in the country of the Indians. Down, down they went on the little trail, in between big rocks and out into the big desert. The trail was so steep that they ran the last part of the way. Then, while they were still running, they went up a little hill covered with gray sage and down into a sandy place where water ran in the time of rains. But now there was no water there, only white sand that felt very firm and nice under their feet. A little dog was in that place. Nah-wee saw him before they came to him, and she very quickly had a sorry feeling for that little dog. He was very thin, and he had a look in the eyes that anyone could tell was a hunger look.

"Oh," said Nah-wee, "how I wish I had food to give to that little dog!" But Dat-say did not say one word. He opened the little bundle of food his mother had given to him and took a piece of the meat and a piece of piki bread and gave them to the dog, and Nah-wee opened her eyes wide to see how quickly that little dog ate it up. Then Dat-say gave him some more, and the dog ate that too, and very quickly there were only the dried apricots left of the bundle of food. Dat-say knew a dog, even a very hungry little dog, would not eat apricots, so he gave half of them to Nah-wee, and he ate the other half himself. And then the little dog did a very queer thing. He looked into the face of Dat-say and barked. And then he turned and ran up the side of the sandy place where they were and waited at the top for Dat-say to come. Nah-wee clapped her hands.

"Look, how he wants us to go to a place," she cried. "Come, Dat-say, we will see where he wants to go." And when they climbed to the top of the sandy place the little dog barked again and ran ahead of them into the desert, and they followed him, and he grew very excited and barked many times, and Nah-wee and Dat-say grew excited too, and wondered where it was that they were going. The little dog ran very fast when he saw that they were following him, and they came after him as fast as they could, but by this time they were almost out of breath. He led them to a great clump of high bushes, and back of the bushes was a queer little home-place made of mud and sticks and clay. There was a door in the place, and the dog went straight in and barked and came out again, waiting at the door for them to come inside. And a voice called then from the inside of the place:

"Ai, but has a someone come at last? I thought never would anyone come." And Dat-say ran into the house then, and a very old woman was there. Nah-wee saw her too. The old woman had hurt her foot and could not move. She was lying on a place made soft with sheepskins.

"Look, how I have a hurt place," she said when she saw the two children. "And I have no food. A little dog cannot bring things to me, and besides, there is no food to bring."

"Oh," said Nah-wee, "how I wish now that we had that food we gave to the little dog!"

"No," said Dat-say, "I will go and get food. I will get plenty for us all. If you will wait here I will go quickly." And as soon as he said that he was gone. And Nah-wee got some water where the old woman told her to get it, and she thought the old woman would never stop drinking when she gave her some in a little pottery bowl.

"I think never was water good like that water," said the

old woman when she had drunk all she could. "Now, already I am very much better." And then Nah-wee made the little house to be very clean. She brushed out the ashes in the cooking place, and she made the sheepskins smooth and comfortable, and the old woman smiled at her. In one corner of the room were many reeds and roots and dried grasses.

"The mother of Dat-say is one who makes baskets," said Nah-wee to the old woman, "and this day we will go and find reeds and grasses like these that you have."

"No," said the old woman very quickly. "You will take these very ones, all of them. I do not make baskets any more, and I do not need these ones." And when Dat-say came back he was very glad to hear that. He brought so much food that the eyes of the old woman turned bright as stars to see it.

"And more will come," he said, "when this is gone. I have told them how you have a hurt place, and one will come who will help you."

The old woman smiled at them when she had eaten, and then she called to Nah-wee to come very close.

"You are a little girl and you will like this," she said. "It is for you to keep always"; and she put into her hand a little string of beads blue as the sky. "And for you," she said to Dat-say, "look—that bow that is hanging on the wall and the arrows that are near it. They are for you. When my boy was little they were for him, but now he is a man and has gone away. And for *you*—" she laughed and gave to the little dog a bone from some of the meat that Dat-say had brought—but there were little wet drops in her eyes when she laughed—"for you there will always be the half of the food that I have, for always you have brought to me good."

"That is a very nice little dog," said Nah-wee to Dat-say when they had left the old woman and were on the home trail again. Dat-say nodded.

"The little dog is good to the woman because the woman is good to the little dog. Always things are like that."

"Yes," laughed Nah-wee. "And your mother, too, will think how the little dog is good when she makes baskets with those grasses that you have brought."

But when the mother of Dat-say was told about the little dog she was quiet for a little and there was a very nice look in her eyes when she looked at Dat-say, and then, it was a strange thing, but she did not say anything about the little dog, she said:

"I have made some very nice seed cakes. Come and see if they are good." And after that no one remembered the little dog at all, not for a very long time.

THE WARRIOR

The very next day, after the adventure of the little dog, Nah-wee and Dat-say were sent down into the peach orchard to gather some peaches. They were very glad to go, for they knew that while they gathered the peaches they could eat as many as they wanted, and they liked peaches very much. Nah-wee put three peaches into the basket and three peaches into Nah-wee and then she thought it was time to rest. Dat-say did not know how many he had eaten, but he knew the sun was very hot, and the shade under the trees looked very cool, so he decided he would sit down by Nah-wee, and then they both rested for a little while. It was very much easier to rest with their eyes closed, and there were bees humming busily in the peach trees, and bees make a very sleepy sound.

"Hum-hum-m-m!" went the bees. So, in a very little while Nah-wee was nodding. And then——! She had a very exciting dream. It was like a tale old Tonto, the story-teller, had once told to her. There was fighting in it! And Indians came very fast on horses riding nearer and nearer! And just then she opened her eyes and saw, off through the trees of the peach orchard, a great warrior on a horse, and he was riding nearer and nearer to her! Nah-wee jumped up from her comfortable place under the tree and cried out to Dat-say in fright:

"Dat-say, look! How warriors are coming! We must run!" and without another look at the man on the horse she ran as fast as she could through the little orchard of trees and through the sage to the place where the home trail started up the big hill, and Dat-say followed after her as fast as he could go. It may be that he too had dreamed a fighting dream like the one she had dreamed, and even yet he was not very sure that he was awake. They both heard that sound of the horse coming after them—"Clicketty-clack! Clicketty-clack!" on the hard, rocky trail, and they grew more and more frightened as they ran. Never before had they seen a man all dressed up for war like this one, with a great bonnet of feathers around his head and hanging down his back. Surely he must be some terrible one from another tribe. Just as they reached the bottom of the hill and their breath was coming very fast and their hearts pounding like little drums, a voice called out to them, and they knew it was the man on the horse who called.

"Hi!" said the voice. "Stop—do not go up that trail!" and it was very strange, but there was a sound in that voice that Nah-wee had heard before. She turned her head just a little bit and looked at the man again. He was very much nearer now, and she could see him much better than she had seen him before. She did not stop running, but she did not run quite so fast. The big feather bonnet looked just as terrible as it had looked before, but the eyes of the man did not look terrible. They were very friendly eyes, and there was a twinkle in them, and then, very suddenly, Nah-wee stopped running altogether and opened her own eyes so wide that they looked almost as big as all the rest of her face.

"Oh," said Nah-wee then, very softly—but Dat-say heard her, and he, too, stopped and looked. "I—I—thought——!" said Nah-wee, and the man made his horse to stand still, and he threw back his head and he laughed so loud that all the hills sent back little laughing sounds, and Nah-wee felt a smile-feeling coming to her own lips. For the man was her very own uncle, only she had not known him because of the war bonnet. He was dressed up to take part in a big dance that Nah-wee had heard her father talking about, and Nah-wee and Dat-say too had begged very hard to go to that dance.

"You can run very fast," said the uncle when he had stopped laughing. "I think, maybe, you could win a race if you would run in one." And the twinkle was still in his eyes. "Maybe you would like to go to that dance where I am going. That is why I have come."

"Oh," cried Nah-wee and Dat-say at the very same time, "more than anything we would like to do that! But it is very far, and we have no horse."

The uncle smiled again.

"My horse cannot carry three ones," he said, "but look

what comes over there." And he pointed back in the little hills where they saw coming a very fat little burro. A man was driving the burro, and he had bundles on his back, but Nah-wee and Dat-say got right up on top of the bundles, and they felt as if they were on top of a hill. But *never* had they been so happy before.

"Come," said the uncle, "already your mothers have said that you could go with me, and we will ride very fast to that dance." And Nah-wee thought that this was the very nicest thing that had ever happened to her.

"Jog-jog-jog—" went the little burro on his stiff little legs, through sage and rocks and sand. And they saw many other people all going the same way that they were going and all dressed in their very brightest and best clothes. Up little hills they rode and down again, far out over the desert that was dressed in its very brightest colors, too, golden sand, and purple sage, and pink hills, and shiny blue sky.

Nah-wee felt that they must be going to the very edge of the world. They rode until the sun was straight up in the middle part of the sky, and then they came to a little town with houses made of adobe clay just like the houses in her very own home town, and there were very many people there and much noise and excitement.

The uncle gave them good things to eat and spread a blanket on a low wall-place and told them to wait in this place until he came again, and then he went away. There was so much to see that Nah-wee and Dat-say grew almost dizzy with watching. And when the dance began there were many men dressed exactly like the uncle, so that Nah-wee rubbed her eyes hard to be sure she was awake.

There was a man who beat on a drum that sounded like thunder and other men shook rattles in time to his beating, and there were men who sang and many who danced. Nah-wee grew so tired of watching so many things that she was glad when the sun went down behind the purple hills and the uncle came back to get them, and they rode away again on the little burro into the quiet evening.

After a while the little star brothers came out in the sky as they rode back on the home trail, and for a long time Nah-wee did not say one word.

"Did you think that was a very nice dance?" asked the uncle then, and he rode very close to her on his horse to hear what she would say. But Nah-wee did not say one word, and when the uncle looked more closely he saw that she was fast asleep.

"I think maybe she ate very many of those seed cakes," said Dat-say, and there was a grin on his face. "Those were very good seed cakes," and he rubbed the front of his own little belt very thoughtfully. And then, when the uncle looked at Dat-say in a little while he could see by the floppy way his head went up and down that he too was maybe dreaming of seed cakes in a faraway land of sleep.

THE LOST PINON TREE ADVENTURE

Nah-wee lived in a stone house with her mother and father. She thought it was a very nice house. It had only one room, but that did not matter: they did not need more than one room. There was the fireplace, with the cooking-stone and all the pottery jars in which the good things to eat were cooked, and they ate them right there on the floor in front of the fire. They slept on a little shelf of rock that ran around two sides of the room, and their blankets and soft sheepskins were all folded neatly in the daytime so that there was plenty of room to sit if visitors came in, and the loom for weaving was just outside the door usually, though in the time of rains it could be kept inside. Nah-wee helped to keep the little house clean, and she was very proud of the fact that even though she was very small she knew how to grind corn, as her mother did, on the metate stone, and she knew how to make the thin cakes of piki bread. One day Nah-wee was sitting in the doorway of her home-place watching her mother weave a bright red blanket when Dat-say came running. He called out when he saw her, "My mother has sent me to get clay for the pottery jars, and I must go quickly, but if you will come maybe we will see a rabbit. Yesterday I saw two rabbits, and soon I will learn to get them with my rabbit stick so that we can have stew."

"Um-m-m! I like rabbit stew," said Nah-wee, and she jumped up quickly from the step. "May I go, my mother?"

Her mother smiled. Always she had smiles for Nah-wee.

"If you will go and come again before the dark is here," she said, "and be very sure that you do not go where you cannot see this place—never go that far away." And Nah-wee was gone almost before she heard those last words. She knew when her mother had smiled that she could go, and she did not wait for the rest. They ran down the trail on the side of the hill. Not ever did they walk when they could run, and they laughed when they saw that their shadows ran ahead of them all the way down the trail.

"Do you see," shouted Dat-say, "how always there are four of us who go? In the middle of the day, when it is time to eat, those shadow ones grow very short and fat, and when the father sun is low behind the hills, how long and thin our brother shadows are."

"Now they are not very thin," answered Nah-wee, "and

they are not very fat," and she said that last a little slowly, "but already I am hungry."

"Ho!" said Dat-say when they reached the bottom of the trail. "If you are hungry we will find piñon nuts. I know where there is a piñon tree with nuts."

"Where is it?" asked Nah-wee eagerly, for very much she liked piñon nuts, and right now she felt that she could eat many of them. "Let us find it quickly."

"It is this way," said Dat-say, and he led the way to a little wash that went straight out into the desert.

A wash is a place where much water has run, like a little river, in the time of rains, but when the rains stop the water runs away and only sand is left. But the water runs in many queer directions, and so a wash goes this way and that

way with many little washes leading out of the first one. And it is a *very* easy place to get lost in—and that is just exactly what happened to Nah-wee and Dat-say.

Very surely Dat-say thought that he knew where that little piñon tree grew. At first they ran down the sandy center of the wash, and it was very nice. They saw many rabbits, and two times they saw little horned toads sunning themselves on the rocks. But they did not see any piñon trees. Dat-say stopped suddenly when they had run for a little while, and a thought look came to his eyes.

"It was not far away like this," he said. "I think that little tree is gone."

"Maybe it is over there," said Nah-wee, and she pointed to a part of the little wash that went out from the one where

they were. Dat-say remembered now that they had passed many places that looked like that, and so they turned around and went back to see if the little piñon tree was up some other way; but always there were so many turns and so many little washes running this way and that, and never any piñon trees, so that after they had looked for a very long time, they were both very tired and sat down on the side of the wash to rest.

"What will we do now?" asked Nah-wee in a very small voice, and Dat-say stood up quickly when she said that and made himself to be as tall as he could.

"You are only a little one," he said. "You must sit here and rest, and I will go and find the way to go back."

"Is that one lost, too?" asked Nah-wee and her eyes were very big and black. "I thought only the way of the piñon tree was lost."

"Not any way is lost," said Dat-say, and he could not help the little grin that came to his face. "Not any way at all is lost. *We* are the ones that are lost," And when he said that a big laugh came from the edge of the wash just back of where they were. And they looked up and saw the very fattest, jolliest kind of a face that looked down at them. Below the face was a fat round body that shook all over when the laugh came out.

"Hi!" said the fat one. "So you are lost! That is a very good tale"; and he laughed again until the tears dropped from his eyes, but Dat-say did not laugh. A very big frown came to his face, and he said to the man:

"Where is the thing that makes you to laugh when a very little one is lost and is very hungry?"

The fat one stopped laughing then, but he reached down

into the wash with one hand for Nah-wee to catch hold of.

"Come up," he said, "come up, and you will see why it is that I laugh." And the little laugh wrinkles were so tight about his eyes that the eyes were almost hidden altogether. Nah-wee and Dat-say climbed out of the wash, and they looked where he pointed, and then they saw why it was that he had laughed, for they were almost as near to the home-place as they had been when they came down the trail. They had gone up the little wash and back again, and one part looked so much like another part that they did not know it and the sandy bank was too high to see over. The fat one made a chuckly sound again, and this time Dat-say looked at him, and he grinned too.

"I did not think to come to the top and look," said Dat-say, and the fat one looked quickly then at Nah-wee.

"I have here," he said, "some things that are very good when that hunger feeling comes," and he ran to a little burro that was standing near and put his hand in a sack on his back and drew out red apples and piñon nuts and many seed cakes, and he gave to Nah-wee and to Dat-say all that they could hold in their hands, and then he got on his little burro and rode away, and he was still laughing as he went.

"I did not mind that he laughed," said Nah-wee. "I think he is a very good man."

"I would laugh too," said Dat-say, "if I had a big sack of apples and a burro and could see over the top of things."

And then they went to get the clay for his mother, and they ate every little bit of the good things the man had given them—except some crumbs that fell in the sage, and two little gray birds were very glad to get *those!*

THE ADVENTURE IN THE CAVE

One morning Dat-say said to Nah-wee, "I have a trap down in the edge of the desert. I am going to see if there is anything in it. I may catch a coyote."

"I will go too," said Nah-wee, and she danced on the tips of her toes because she was so happy to go. All this morning she had wanted very much to go down into the desert, but her mother would not let her go alone. When she had first opened her eyes and looked out at the golden sunshine and the blue sky and the white puffy clouds that were racing before the wind, she had thought how nice it would be to run down in the desert and find little stones of bright colors and watch the rabbits pop into the sage and eat piñon nuts and little berries that Dat-say knew how to find. Every day the desert seemed to be a different place to Nah-wee, and always there were so many things to do. And if Dat-say had made a trap it was very exciting to think what might be the thing that was in it. As they ran down the trail, Nah-wee could see little puffs of dust in the desert, and far away, behind the blue hills, were great white clouds piled high in the sky.

"I like to see the clouds like that," she said to Dat-say. "I think maybe they are very big birds. I would like to feel how their feathers are soft."

"I think they are not birds," said Dat-say. "They are big white blankets, and they are full of water. My father says it will rain."

"It does not matter," laughed Nah-wee. "Water is nice and my mother says it is the rain that makes the corn and the melons to grow."

"Water is nice when it is not falling down on you out of the sky," laughed Dat-say. "But look now, how the clouds are not white any more."

"BOOM-m!" went a big sound then, and Nah-wee and Dat-say both gave a jump. They were out in the desert now, very near to the place where the trap of Dat-say was laid.

"It is the Thunder Drum of the rain," said Dat-say. "Now will come the dance of the water. I think maybe it would be the best thing to go back up that trail."

"First we must see what is in the trap," begged Nah-wee. "Never have I seen a wild animal that is alive—maybe one is there." But when they got to the trap nothing was there at all. Dat-say could see very plainly that a something had been there, but now it was gone, and a little he was glad that it was so. Never had he caught a live thing, and he did not very much like the thought of it.

"BOOM! BOOM!" went that thunder sound again, and little drops of rain began to come down.

"Now we will get very wet," said Dat-say. "There is no place on that trail where the rain cannot come."

"But look!" said Nah-wee, and she pointed to a place on the side of the hill where a big flat rock stuck out in such a way that there was a shelter-place under it like a little room; "I think maybe we could get under that rock." And they both ran to the place, and they got under the rock before the very hardest rain came. There was just room enough for them both, and they were very glad to be there, for never had the rain come down harder than this time. It was like a river coming straight out of the sky, and they could not see anything outside of their little shelter-place at all. Then Dat-say gave a little cry.

"Look!" he said. "There is a hole back of this rock. I think it is a cave-place. I will see if I can go in." And sure enough there was a black hole that went into the side of the hill, and he put his head inside and began to crawl in, and Nah-wee watched him eagerly. Maybe there would be room inside for her to come too, and a cave was a very nice thing to find. But when Dat-say was half inside he backed out again so quickly that he went right out into the rain, and he gave a little howl of surprise.

"There is a thing in that place!" he cried. "A live thing! I felt how it moved. It went against my face!"

"What is it?" cried Nah-wee, and she did not mind that

the rain came down hard on them both.

"Maybe it is a bear!" said Dat-say, but then he knew very quickly that it could not be a bear. A bear could not go into a place that was so small, and almost any animal that he knew would have bitten him or would have growled when he came so close. He felt very curious about this one, and then suddenly he got down on his hands and knees again by the hole. "I think," he said, "I will go in and see what it is."

"Oh, no!" cried Nah-wee. "Do not go in that place again. Come out, Dat-say"; and she caught hold of his arm and tried to pull him back. "Maybe it will eat you up." But already Dat-say was in that hole, and he felt very brave to have Nah-wee talk like that, but he did not have any fear of this thing in the cave—it could not be a very big thing. This time

he reached in with his hands, and he brought out that live thing, and Nah-wee cried out when she saw it. It was very small and very soft and very brown. It was a BABY COYOTE!

"Oh!" said Nah-wee. "Oh, Dat-say! Let me put my hands on it!" It trembled when she touched it and tried to get away.

"I think the mother has been caught in some trap," said Dat-say. "Not ever will I make a trap again. And this one will maybe starve if we do not feed it. We must go fast up that trail. My mother will know the thing to do." And they forgot that the rain still came down very hard, and they forgot that the trail was steep, and remembered only to keep that little coyote very warm and dry in the dress of Nah-wee.

And Nah-wee all the time made little soft sounds with her mouth to feel that warm little thing so close.

Many people in the town came to see that little coyote and said it was a good thing that Dat-say had found it, for it was very hungry, and the mother must have been gone a long time. It could not have lived without the food they gave to it. But it did live, and grew to be tame like a little dog, so that it followed Nah-wee and Dat-say wherever they went, and not *ever* after that did Dat-say put any trap in the desert. He thought if he did that maybe he would catch some other mother coyote, and maybe somewhere a baby coyote would wait for food and no one would come.

"Traps are not good," said Dat-say, and Nah-wee nodded her head solemnly.

"For me," she said, "I like much better a little cave-place," and she looked very wise when she said it.

A VERY QUEER ADVENTURE

Almost better than anything else in the world Nah-wee liked a stew made of rabbit meat. Her mother could make a very good stew, and when she stirred it in the big pot a little trail of smell would go out on the air, winding here and there, and Nah-wee would always find that smell-trail and would follow it home no matter where she was. This very day there was a rabbit stew cooking in the pot, and Nah-wee thought that *never* would the time come when it would be done. She had waited and sniffed at that good smell for so long that the hunger-feeling was almost the very biggest part of her—and she felt as if she could eat all there was in the pot. Her mother and her father had said many things about a dance that

would be down in the desert this night, and Nah-wee was to go with them. She liked very much to go to a dance at night. The men would sing all together, and one would beat on a drum, and there would be a very big campfire and much laughing and talking, and after that they would dance and eat good things. Yes, a dance was very nice, but first would come a supper of rabbit stew from the big iron pot, and Nah-wee smacked her lips at the thought.

At last her mother called out to her that it was ready, and her father came in and sat down by the fire, and they were given little pottery bowls of the delicious stew. Nah-wee ate and ate, and her mother watched her and smiled, and when the little bowl grew empty she filled it up again. And it grew empty very many times. But after a while—a very long while—Nah-wee could not eat any more. That was very strange, for there was still much stew in the pot, but a stranger thing yet was to happen. Nah-wee sat for a long time in front of the fire and watched the little yellow flames jump and dance and the black shadows fly up and down on the wall, and she felt very comfortable—not *ever* had she felt more comfortable. The blanket that she sat on was soft and warm and *everything* felt soft and warm. She closed her eyes just for a minute and imagined she could hear drum sounds and people talking. AND THIS IS THE STRANGE THING! In a little while—it *seemed* like a very little while—while Nah-wee was still feeling very comfortable, her father gave her arm a little shake and he said to her:

"Did you like that dance, Nah-wee?"

That was a very funny thing to say, and Nah-wee blinked her eyes hard and opened them wide. What did that father

mean? Was it the little dance of the flames in the fireplace that he talked about?

"What is that dance that you talk about?" asked Nah-wee, and when she said that her father laughed so loud that the little pottery jars on the hearth-place gave a jiggly jump, and her mother laughed too, only her laugh was much smaller and had giggly sounds in it.

"Hi!" said her father, and he could hardly talk because he laughed so much. "Hear what it is that this little one says, 'What dance is that?' And all this very night we have watched the dance in the desert, and little Nah-wee lay warm in a blanket and dreamed of rabbit stew, and not even the pounding of the drum could awaken her. Never did I know a little one could sleep like that." And it was true. That was the strange thing that had happened to Nah-wee. She went to a dance in the desert and she did not know it. And after that, when Nah-wee ate rabbit stew she was very careful not to eat too much and not to sit by the fire afterwards and watch the dancing flames. For she did not want to go to sleep again and miss things—AND SHE NEVER DID!

Let's Visit South Africa

At the southern tip of Africa lies the Union of South Africa. It is a beautiful land of snow-capped mountains, tropical forests, rolling prairies, and blue lakes. Its wonderful mild and dry climate makes this country one of the healthiest places in which to live.

The Dutch were the first to settle at the Cape of Good Hope in 1652. Almost at the same time they were starting a colony on the island of Manhattan in America! In South Africa, they found tribes of tiny wild men called Bushmen and Hottentots. Later, the British captured the Cape and the Dutch settlers moved inland. Today, South Africa has many European people, but most of its population is native African. Fierce tribesmen, like the Zulus, have become peaceful farmers who raise sheep and grow corn. Some Africans live on great reserves which are tracts of land like the Indian reservations in the United States. There, tribal life has changed very little; the chief still makes the decisions. Other natives have gone to the large industrial centers to work in modern factories or in the great mines which produce most of the world's diamonds and half of the world's gold.

South Africa is also rich in coal, iron, uranium–and all kinds of wild animals. In Kruger National Park, you can see a huge hippopotamus and dangerous African lions roam about as freely as they wish! The Union of South Africa used to be a part of the British Commonwealth, but became an independent republic in 1961.

The Flag of South Africa

You can always tell a Basuto "cowboy" by his vividly colored blankets, his saucer-shaped hat, and his broad flashing smile.

This Zulu woman likes to put on bright "war paint" for important occasions. She pulls her hair high on her head, and builds it up with wool, grass and red mud clay until it looks like an "upside down" pudding! Then she sews colored strings and beads into it for strength and decoration.

ATLANTIC OCEAN
SOUTHWEST AFRICA
FORBIDDEN COAST
1
AUGHRABIES FAL
(HUNDRED FALLS
ORANGE RIVER
9
CAPE OF GOOD HOPE
CAPETOWN
7
KIMBE
CANGO CAVES
5
FLYING DUTCHMAN
4 OSTRICH FARM AND TSITSIKAMA FOREST
ADD
ELEP
NATIO
6
PORT ELIZABETH
12
EAST
N
W
E
S
INDIAN

Can you find the following things on this map of South Africa? **1.** Diamonds on the Forbidden Coast **2.** Wild animals in Kruger National Park **3.** Zulu tribesman **4.** Ostrich farm **5.** House of Parliament **6.** Pigmy elephant **7.** Flowering desert cacti **8.** Swaziland native **9.** 100 waterfalls on the Orange River **10.** N'debeles native wearing bright copper rings **11.** City of Gold **12.** Port Elizabeth lighthouse **13.** Africa's "radio," the drum **14.** Bantu dance ceremony

Capetown is the oldest city in this modern country. Its harbor is one of the most beautiful in the whole world.

Bushmen were among the earliest men in South Africa. They lived on roots, berries, and animals killed with poison arrows.

Printed in the United States of America